The ARTIST'S
MARKETING & ACTION PLAN
WORKBOOK

To Marsha, Loren, and Garret

BOOKS BY JONATHAN TALBOT

Collage: A New Approach

The Artist's Marketing & Action Plan Workbook

THE ARTIST'S MARKETING & ACTION PLAN WORKBOOK

Revised 5th Edition

by

JONATHAN TALBOT

with

GEOFFREY HOWARD

Illustrations by

LOEL BARR

Book copyright © 1999-2005 by Jonathan Talbot
Illustrations copyright © 2005 by Loel Barr

This Edition Published in 2005 by Jonathan Talbot,
7 Amity Road, Warwick, NY 10990
Phone: (845) 258-4620 E-mail: jonathan@talbot1.com Internet: www.talbot1.com

Some of the information in the appendix is subject to change.
A free download of the most recently updated version of that information is available at
www.artistsworkbook.com

Talbot, Jonathan and Howard, Geoffrey
Artist's Marketing and Action Plan Workbook / Jonathan Talbot
Includes Appendix
ISBN 0-9701681-3-6
1. Art — Marketing I. Title
706'.8'8 — dc20

❧ ❧ ❧ ❧

5th Edition – First Printing — January 2005
Printed and Bound by Royal Fireworks, Unionville, NY
1 2 3 4 5 6 7 8 9 0

JONATHAN TALBOT

Jonathan Talbot is an artist whose works have been exhibited at The National Academy and The Museum of Modern Art in New York, have represented the U.S. overseas in exhibitions sponsored by the State Department and the Smithsonian Institution, and are included in museum collections in the U.S. and Europe.
Jonathan Talbot's work may be seen at www.talbot1.com

GEOFFREY HOWARD

Geoffrey Howard is an internationally known consultant in marketing, customer service, and strategic planning. His clients have included Citibank, HBO, Chase, Weyerhauser, Hercules Chemical, Deutsche Bank and Pepsico.

LOEL BARR (Illustrator)

Loel Barr is an award-winning illustrator whose work appears in numerous publications. After many years in Washington DC, she now resides in New York's Hudson Valley where she also works on her own paintings, collages, and digital art.
See Loel Barr's work at www.loelbarr.com

SCOTT FRAY (Cover Design)

Scott Fray is an artist, illustrator, multimedia developer and bodypainter. He has worked for Coke, Pepsi, Fox News, National Geographic, History Channel, Balantine Books, Wrangler, Winston Cup Racing, and more. He is happiest when sitting atop an extinct volcano in Iceland or on the black shores of Antarctica.
Find out more about Scott, his art, work, and travels at www.scottfray.com

With special thanks to MARY DI STASIO and LAURA BREITMAN whose insights proved invaluable to the successful completion of this project.

There is no reason why that which affords you the
highest pleasure should not also become a source of income.

No one deserves success more than you do.
This does not mean that you deserve success more than anyone else.
It means exactly what it says —
No one deserves success more than you do.

One need not sell one's soul in order to sell one's art.

CONTENTS

APPENDIX

INTRODUCTION:

WHAT'S THE POINT?

This book has been written to help you become more skilled at the art of selling your work. It is a workbook, a book to write in. It will guide you through the process of learning how to sell your work and HOW TO MAKE MONEY DOING IT!

The making of art and the selling of art are essentially different. For most of us, art making is intensely personal and private. Only when we are finished are we willing to share what we have done. Selling art is, on the other hand, a social activity in which we are required to interact with the world outside our studios. This book provides a structure and vocabulary for that interaction.

When you have finished doing the exercises and using the forms in this book, you will have a *personalized*, step-by-step marketing and action plan for selling your work.

Many artists find satisfaction in selling their work. Some of their reasons are:

> To validate the art making experience.
> To make room in the studio.
> For the recognition that comes from sales.
> To be considered professional.
> To consider oneself professional.
> To impress one's family, friends, or other artists.
> To buy more materials.
> So the world will see the work.
> To make money.

Whether your motivation appears in the list above, or if it is something entirely different, this book will be useful to you.

Each of us must put some effort into getting our work "out there" in order for the work to find an audience. Michelangelo had to argue with the Pope in order get paid for painting the ceiling of the Sistine Chapel. Artemesia had to fight the misogyny of 17th Century Italy in order to practice her art. Picasso was an excellent businessman. Mary Cassat carved a niche for herself in impressionist art circles by showing American collectors around Paris. Dali was a flamboyant showman, as was Andy Warhol. Most well-known artists are or have been effective self-promoters.

Much of the information which I have included in this book has been learned the hard way, by my own mistakes. I am comforted by remembering that the only "bad" mistakes we make are the ones from which we do not learn. Nevertheless, despite all I have learned during my thirty-four years as a full-time visual artist, I could not have written this book without the benefits of Geoffrey Howard's marketing expertise and Mary Di Stasio's knowledge of economics.

In addition to the exercise pages and the action plan forms, this book includes an appendix of useful information and sample press releases, etc. Some of the information in the appendix (addresses of arts councils, publications, etc.) is subject to change. For a free download of the most recently updated version of this information visit www.artistsworkbook.com

I am interested in your feedback. If you have comments about this book or suggestions for ways in which it can be improved, e-mail me at feedback@artistsworkbook.com or write me at the address on the copyright page.

> — Jonathan Talbot
> Warwick, NY, 2005

Write your name and the date in the spaces provided.
This is your workbook and the Marketing and Action Plan you create
will be custom made for you.

_____

(name)

CREATED THIS
MARKETING AND ACTION PLAN
IN

_____

(month & year)

PART I:
LOOKING IN THE MIRROR

1. Why are You an Artist? | 2. Artists You Admire. | 3. What does Success "look like" for You?

1. WHY ARE YOU AN ARTIST?

More than twenty years ago I was dining with two artist-friends and a dealer who represented two of us. The dealer asked each of us "why are you an artist?" The answers were surprisingly varied. One of us said "I'm just in it for the money. I'll paint whatever people will buy." Another said "I want to get my artwork into museums, to carve a niche for myself in posterity." The third said "I just want to make enough money with my paintings so I can go fishing once in a while."

Knowing why you are an artist is important to the development of your Marketing and Action Plan.

Why are you an artist? What role do you want art to play in your life? The following options may help you to focus...

Check the boxes that are most important to you (You can check them all if you wish but that will not help the process as much as choosing those that are most important to you.)

Art is:

☐ Easy	☐ Sexy	☐ Satisfying
☐ Serious	☐ Profound	☐ Something that requires talent
☐ Fun	☐ Unnecessary	☐ Something anyone can do
☐ Important	☐ Enjoyable	☐ Something few folks can do
☐ Respectable	☐ Relaxing	☐ Something I like to do alone
☐ Rewarding	☐ Moving	☐ Something I like to do with others
☐ Difficult	☐ Enlightening	☐ Something I do for myself
☐ Empowering	☐ Frustrating	☐ Something I do for others

Check the statements you believe to be true (Check as many as you wish).

☐ Art in museums is good   ☐ Better artists make more money

☐ Most artists are poor   ☐ Most art galleries treat artists fairly

☐ Many artists are rich   ☐ Most art galleries treat artists unfairly

☐ Good art sells   ☐ Successful artists must compromise their principles

☐ Bad art sells   ☐ People aren't interested in art any more

☐ Art is necessary   ☐ I can't make a good living as an artist

☐ Art is unnecessary   ☐ Only rich people buy art

☐ Art is fulfilling   ☐ Anyone can be an artist

☐ Artists enjoy life   ☐ Artists are impulsive

☐ Artists suffer   ☐ Artists are compulsive

☐ Artists have fun   ☐ Artists work with their hands

☐ Artists have free time   ☐ Artists are sensitive

☐ Artists work hard   ☐ Artists are difficult to live with

☐ Artists are noble   ☐ Artists are inspired

☐ Artists are messy   ☐ Artists enjoy working alone

☐ Artists are lazy   ☐ Artists are generous

☐ Artists are lonely   ☐ Artists want to make money

☐ Artists are crazy   ☐ Artists can express themselves

☐ Artists deserve grants   ☐ Art is a road to immortality

☐ Art is a road to fame   ☐ Solo exhibitions are profitable

☐ Art is important   ☐ The life of an artist is exciting

☐ Art is communication   ☐ Art is a road to recognition

☐ Artists are selfish   ☐ Artists must sacrifice everything for art

☐ Artists are born that way   ☐ Artists are only famous after they're dead

☐ Artists are important   ☐ Artists are unsatisfied

☐ Art can be taught   ☐ Everything artistic has been done already

☐ Art is special   ☐ Artists are irresponsible

☐ Artists get respect   ☐ Artists are introspective

☐ A degree in art is helpful   ☐ Artists contribute to society

☐ Artists are different   ☐ Artists are undisciplined

☐ Art is for kids   ☐ The arts have less gender bias than other professions

☐ Art is for seniors   ☐ If you can make art you must do it

☐ Artists are neurotic   ☐ Art education doesn't matter

☐ Art can make a difference   ☐ Artists are anti-establishment

Check the boxes that best describe you

☐ I am an artist	☐ I have good business skills	☐ I am driven to make art
☐ I am a would-be artist	☐ I want to make money	☐ I want my art to communicate
☐ I want fame	☐ I want to express myself	☐ I want to contribute to society
☐ I want recognition	☐ I want immortality	☐ I have good business skills
☐ I have time for my art	☐ I want contentment	☐ I am _____
☐ I have talent	☐ I want to show my art	☐ I am _____
☐ I like making art	☐ I don't want to show my art	☐ I am _____
☐ I love making art	☐ I don't have time for my art	☐ I am _____

Why you are an Artist:

Now, looking over the boxes you have checked, complete the statement below. Try to be concise and limit your writing to the space provided. Use the margins if necessary:

I am an artist because

....

....

....

....

....

....

....

....

....

....

....

....

2. ARTISTS YOU ADMIRE

Knowing who you respect can often tell you a lot about yourself. Write the names of some artists you hold in high esteem in the spaces below. They may be famous artists and/or artists you know personally but keep in mind that this question asks for *artists* you admire, not *artists whose artwork* you admire. For example, you may admire the artwork of Vincent Van Gogh, but would you want to have lived his life? The goal of this question is to identify some artists you might accept as role models both for their work and the way they lived their lives. *Fill in as many blanks as you wish. If there are not enough lines, use the margins of the paper. If you don't fill the lines it's OK. You can always add more names later.*

Some artists I admire are:

_____

_____

_____

_____

_____

_____

_____

_____

_____

From the list on the previous page, pick the artist about whom you know the most and write his or her name in the space provided below. Once again, keep in mind that you are being asked to write the name of the *artist* you know the most about, not the *artist whose work* you know the most about.

_____

Why do you hold this artist in high esteem? *Be as specific as you can. What are the characteristics of this artist that make her or him attractive to you? What do you know about his or her professional life? What do you know about his or her personal life?*

I admire *(write name of artist here)* _____

because: _____

_____

_____

_____

_____

_____

_____

_____

_____

_____

_____

Record below those characteristics (if any) of the artist you admire that are part of you and/or your life or which you would like to become part of you and/or your life.

3. WHAT DOES SUCCESS LOOK LIKE FOR YOU?

Now, more than twenty years later, the artists I mentioned in the introduction to this section are still friends and we are still full-time artists. The dealer is no longer in business but we have continued to flourish. One of us "paints to the market," producing exactly what the public wants, and delights in spending the money he earns. Another of us has managed to get his works into some museums and important private collections and is happy about that. The third paints five days a week, spends weekends hunting and fishing, and often chooses wildlife as the subjects of his paintings.

Each of us has achieved success as he or she defines it, but our definitions differ. A clear picture of what personal success means to you is important to the development of your Marketing and Action Plan.

What does success mean to you? The following options may help you to clarify the picture.

Check those boxes which you consider important parts of your picture of success. Check as many as you wish. Some blanks are left for you to add your own possibilities. Note: There may be some overlap with your answers to previous questions. This may be a sign that you have already achieved some success.

For me, success as an artist includes:

- ☐ Earning a living from my art
- ☐ Being rich
- ☐ Enjoying what I do
- ☐ Having ample time for my art
- ☐ Having work in museums
- ☐ Traveling
- ☐ Being respected by the public
- ☐ Having Fun
- ☐ Having shows
- ☐ Being famous
- ☐ Getting a teaching job
- ☐ Making great works
- ☐ Serving the community
- ☐ Meeting other artists
- ☐ Enjoying myself
- ☐ Enjoying nature
- ☐ Living a long life
- ☐ Being Recognized
- ☐ Winning Awards
- ☐ Living in the country
- ☐ Living in the city
- ☐ Having health insurance
- ☐ A secure retirement
- ☐ Raising a family
- ☐ Having control of my career
- ☐ Doing satisfying work
- ☐ Being remembered
- ☐ Being content

- ☐ Having people write about me
- ☐ Getting reviews
- ☐ Selling a little art
- ☐ Selling some art
- ☐ Selling lots of art
- ☐ Making lots of money
- ☐ Learning new things all the time
- ☐ Adding something to the history of art
- ☐ Having time to do other things besides art
- ☐ Balancing my art with my other interests
- ☐ Feeling good about myself
- ☐ Being excited about my work
- ☐ Being respected by other artists
- ☐ Challenging myself
- ☐ Sharing responsibilities
- ☐ Getting a degree
- ☐ Changing my life
- ☐ Having more time to myself
- ☐ Finding the truth
- ☐ Feeling good about my work
- ☐ Getting listed in Who's Who

- ☐ _____
- ☐ _____
- ☐ _____

From the boxes you have checked in the previous section, select the seven items which are the most important to you and write them below.

Elements
Important
to My
Success

_____

_____

_____

_____

_____

From the seven items above, select the three which are the most important and write them below.

My Goals

_____

_____

From the list above, select the most important item and write it below. Remember, this is your plan as of today, not necessarily forever, so add the date in the space provided at the left. You can change it in the future.

My Main
Goal
as of

_____

_____
Date

We will revisit the subject of goals again but, for the moment, let's move on.

PART II:
LOOKING AT YOUR ART

1. What is your art?

1. WHAT IS YOUR ART?

Art comes in an almost unlimited variety of forms. Developing an effective Marketing/Action Plan requires that you have a clear picture of what it is that you make and wish to market.

The following list may a) help you see your art more clearly and b) help you learn how others see it.

In this section check the boxes that most correctly describe your art. Check as many boxes as you wish.

My Art is:

☐ Visual	☐ Ahead of its time	☐ Fragile	☐ Political	☐ Realistic
☐ Non-Visual	☐ Graphic Design	☐ Not-Fragile	☐ Peaceful	☐ Made Quickly
☐ Transitory	☐ Fits in my car	☐ High Priced	☐ Legal	☐ Made Slowly
☐ Drawings	☐ Wind Sensitive	☐ Low Priced	☐ Illegal	☐ Handmade
☐ Paintings	☐ Medium scale	☐ Production	☐ Seasonal	☐ Precious
☐ Sculptures	☐ Found Objects	☐ Mixed Media	☐ Profound	☐ Humorous
☐ Prints	☐ Revolutionary	☐ Traditional	☐ Ethnic	☐ Therapeutic
☐ Pretty	☐ Uncategorizable	☐ Dangerous	☐ Spiritual	☐ Provocative
☐ Indoor	☐ Non-Functional	☐ Installations	☐ Religious	☐ For Kitchens
☐ Outdoor	☐ Shippable by UPS	☐ Erotic	☐ Watercolor	☐ Commercial
☐ Collages	☐ Shippable by truck	☐ Monotype	☐ Nautical	☐ Small scale
☐ Book Arts	☐ Light (weight)	☐ Photography	☐ Lasting	☐ Includes text
☐ Wearable	☐ Heavy (weight)	☐ Wildlife Art	☐ Ugly	☐ Large scale
☐ Folk art	☐ For adults only	☐ Constructions	☐ Fantasy	☐ Cartoons
☐ Portraits	☐ Primarily for children	☐ Illustration	☐ Satisfying	☐ Caricatures
☐ Unique	☐ For special occasions	☐ Respectable	☐ Laser cut	☐ Calligraphy
☐ Sexy	☐ Has Regional Appeal	☐ Needs Frames	☐ Nostalgic	☐ Digital
☐ Safe	☐ Meant to be touched	☐ Corporate	☐ Escapist	☐ Outsider art
☐ Woven	☐ Copied from others	☐ Collectable	☐ Landscapes	☐ Neon
☐ Edible	☐ Copied by others	☐ Decorative	☐ Paper	☐ Trendy
☐ Fiber Arts	☐ Requires explanation	☐ Collaborative	☐ Animal	☐ Fun
☐ Craft	☐ Hard to understand	☐ Seascapes	☐ Figurative	☐ Functional
☐ Pottery	☐ Computer Generated	☐ One-of-a-kind	☐ Serious	☐ Glass
☐ Ceramics	☐ Environmentally Safe	☐ Performance	☐ Airbrush	☐ _____
☐ Jewelry	☐ Requires electricity	☐ Emotional	☐ Upsetting	☐ _____
☐ Mail Art	☐ Primarily for homes	☐ Western Art	☐ Militant	☐ _____
☐ Toxic	☐ Primarily for offices	☐ Intellectual	☐ Military	☐ _____
☐ Non-Toxic	☐ Primarily for museums	☐ Woodworking	☐ Sincere	☐ _____
☐ Metal	☐ About people	☐ Automotive	☐ Baked	☐ _____
☐ Abstract	☐ Has Multiple Uses	☐ Beaded	☐ Floral	☐ _____

Now, looking over the boxes you have checked, complete the statement below. Try to be concise and limit your writing to the space provided but use the extra space if necessary:

My art is

PART III:
LOOKING AT THE MARKET

1. Who Are Your Clients? | 2. Where Will They Buy Your Works?
3. When Will They Buy Your Works? | 4. How Will They Buy Your Works?

1. WHO ARE YOUR CLIENTS?

You have looked at yourself and you have looked at your art. Now you need to look at your clients, the folks you want to sell our art to.

You can sell your art directly to your clients, or you can employ galleries or dealers to sell your art work for you.

The following checklist will help you determine to whom you want to sell your artworks. It does not answer the question of whether you wish galleries and dealers to be involved. That will be covered later.

Check the boxes of the categories of people or institutions to whom you would like to sell your art. Check as many boxes as you wish.

- ☐ "Regular" Folks
- ☐ Art Collectors
- ☐ Corporations
- ☐ Museums
- ☐ Family
- ☐ Friends
- ☐ Interior Decorators
- ☐ Art Consultants
- ☐ Young Couples
- ☐ Students
- ☐ Restaurants
- ☐ Hotels
- ☐ Publishers (as illustration)

- ☐ Governmental Agencies
- ☐ Artists
- ☐ Educational Institutions
- ☐ Advertising Agencies (as illustration)
- ☐ Newspapers (as illustration)
- ☐ Stock Houses (Photography)
- ☐ Art Publishers (for reproduction)
- ☐ Music Industry (for album covers)
- ☐ Greeting Card Publishers (as illustration)
- ☐ Folks who are interested in the subject matter of the works
- ☐ Folks who are interested in the style of the works
- ☐ Folks who are interested in the techniques of the works
- ☐ Folks who are interested in the media of the works

In this section try to limit your choices to the people or institutions to whom you would most like to sell your art.

Individual Demographics...	Their Household Incomes...	Corporate or Institutional Art Budgets...
☐ Singles	☐ Under $20,000 / yr.	☐ Under $50,000 / yr.
☐ Couples	☐ $20,000 - $40,000 / yr.	☐ $50,000 - $100,000 / yr.
☐ Families	☐ $40,000 - $75,000 / yr.	☐ $100,000 - $250,000 / yr.
☐ Seniors	☐ $75,000 - $125,000 / yr.	☐ $250,000 - $1,000,000 / yr.
☐ Students	☐ $125,000 - $250,000 / yr.	☐ $1,000,,000 - $5,000,000 / yr.
☐ Others	☐ $250,000 - $1,000,000 / yr.	☐ Over $5,000,000 / yr.
	☐ Over $1,000,000 / yr.	

2. WHERE WILL THEY BUY YOUR WORKS?

The following checklist will help you determine where the clients will buy your works.
Check the locations where your art will be sold. Check as many boxes as you wish.

☐ In my Studio	☐ In New York	☐ From Slides
☐ In Galleries	☐ In Los Angeles	☐ From Catalogs
☐ Through Private Dealers	☐ In Provincetown	☐ Door to Door
☐ At Outdoor Art Fairs	☐ In San Francisco	☐ Family Referrals
☐ At Mall Art Fairs	☐ In Paris	☐ In Restaurants
☐ Locally	☐ In London	☐ Solo Exhibitions
☐ Nationally	☐ In Tokyo	☐ Group Exhibitions
☐ Internationally	☐ In Singapore	☐ Theme Exhibitions
☐ In the City	☐ In the Mountains	☐ Tourist Areas
☐ In the Country	☐ At the Shore	☐ In my state
☐ Through Magazines	☐ On the Internet	☐ Direct Mail
☐ _____	☐ _____	☐ _____

3. WHEN WILL THEY BUY YOUR WORKS?

The following checklist will help you determine when the clients will buy your works.
Check as many boxes as you wish in this section.

☐ All Year 'Round
☐ Seasonally *(Particularly applicable to resort areas)*

    ☐ Spring   *Why:*_____
    ☐ Summer *Why:*_____
    ☐ Fall   *Why:*_____
    ☐ Winter *Why:*_____

☐ When I have a Show
☐ Once a Year *(at annual events)*
☐ On Occasion
☐ When I am Visiting Their Area
☐ When They are Visiting My Area
☐ In Connection with Other Events

    ☐ At Fundraising Events   ☐ At Town Celebrations
    ☐ At Flower Shows   ☐ At Theme Festivals
    ☐ At County Fairs   ☐ At Charity Auctions
    ☐ At Car Shows   ☐ Other_____

4. HOW WILL THEY PAY FOR YOUR WORKS?

The following checklist will help you determine how the clients will buy your works.

Check as many boxes as you wish in this section.

☐ Cash   ☐ Credit Card   ☐ Barter

☐ Check   ☐ Time Payments   ☐ Other: _____

5. WHY WILL THEY BUY YOUR WORKS?

The following checklist will help you determine why the clients will buy your works.

Check as many boxes as you wish in this section.

☐ Because they Like Them   ☐ For a Private Collection   ☐ For Prestige

☐ Because of their Subject   ☐ For a Public Collection   ☐ To Resell

☐ For Emotional Content   ☐ For Investment   ☐ As Souvenirs

☐ For Intellectual Content   ☐ For Personal Gifts   ☐ Other: _____

☐ For Decoration   ☐ For Business Gifts   _____

6. HOW LONG WILL IT TAKE THEM TO BUY YOUR WORKS?

Sometimes making a sale takes a considerable amount of time. This is especially true in the case of commissions and sales to institutions or committees. The following checklist will help you determine who long it will take to make a sale. Not all sales will require the same amount of time but some will definitely take longer than others.

Check as many boxes as you wish in this section.

☐ Five Minutes   ☐ Half a Day   ☐ A Week

☐ Fifteen Minutes   ☐ A Day   ☐ Longer than a Week

☐ An Hour   ☐ Overnight   ☐ _____

6. YOUR TARGET MARKETS

Review your answers to questions 1 through 5 — the "who, where, when, how, and why" questions. To what kind of clients you most want to sell your works? That is your Primary Target Market. *Identify your Primary Target Market in the space provided.*

My Primary Target Market is:

Now consider other kinds of clients to whom you hope to sell your works. They are your Secondary Target Markets. *Identify your Secondary Target Markets in the space provided.*

My Secondary Target Markets are:

PART IV:
MARKETING METHODS

1. Connecting with Clients | 2. Pricing Your Works | 3. Determining Total Fixed Costs
4. Determining Average Fixed Cost | 5. Determining Per Unit Variable Cost | 6. Pricing Methods

1. CONNECTING WITH CLIENTS

There are a number of options for getting your artwork and your clients together.

Invitations to Studio: You can invite individuals or small groups to visit your studio and see your work.

Open Studio Events: You can open your studio to the public at specific times or on specific occasions. You can send out invitations to individuals at the same time.

Solo Shows In Galleries: You can have a solo exhibition in a gallery.

Ongoing Gallery Exhibits: Some galleries, particularly those where the clientele is always changing (in tourist areas, for example), do not have shows but keep artists' works on display on an ongoing basis.

Juried Exhibitions: There are lots and lots of juried exhibitions in the U.S. and abroad which one can enter. Usually there are entry fees.

Private Dealers: Private dealers function like galleries but do not have exhibition space. They do have a group of clients with whom they normally work.

Benefit Art Shows: Many religious and sectarian organizations host benefit art shows as a way of making money.

Direct Mail: You can send flyers, brochures, or other mailing pieces showing your work to a wide variety of folks. You can purchase lists of folks who conform to particular demographic patterns.

Mall Art Fairs: Now that malls have replaced the village greens of America, there are art fairs in malls.

Family Referrals: Often members of your family will know someone who may buy your work.

The Internet: The internet is touted as being the fastest growing marketplace in the world.

Magazine Advertising: Some art works, especially works with subject matter that appeals to a particular group and which can be reproduced on a small scale, can be sold through magazine ads.

Outdoor Art Fairs: Outdoor art fairs are big business. Some folks make a good living doing only outdoor shows.

Social Affairs: If you are a good at socializing, you can meet prospective clients at parties, openings, etc.

Restaurant Exhibits: You can show your work in restaurants or other non-gallery settings.

College and University Galleries: Many colleges and universities have exhibition spaces. Sometimes those spaces are host exhibits by non-university artists.

Auctions: You can sell your work at art, general, or internet auctions.

CONNECTING WITH CLIENTS (CONTINUED)

Check the first box if you already use a particular approach. Check the second box if you do not use a particular approach, but would like to use it in the future. Make up your own approaches in the blanks provided.

	Already Use	Use in Future
Invitations to Studio	☐	☐
Open Studio Events	☐	☐
Solo Shows in Galleries	☐	☐
Ongoing Gallery Exhibits	☐	☐
Juried Exhibitions	☐	☐
Private Dealers	☐	☐
Benefit Art Shows	☐	☐
Outdoor Art Fairs	☐	☐
Mall Art Fairs	☐	☐
Family Referrals	☐	☐
The Internet	☐	☐
Magazine Ads	☐	☐
Direct Mail	☐	☐
Catalogs	☐	☐
Social Affairs	☐	☐
Restaurant Exhibits	☐	☐
College & University Galleries	☐	☐
Auctions	☐	☐
Leading Workshops	☐	☐
Presenting Demonstrations	☐	☐
Other: _____	☐	☐
Other: _____	☐	☐
Other: _____	☐	☐
Other: _____	☐	☐

2. PRICING YOUR WORKS

In order to effectively price your work you have to know why you are selling it. Refer back to pages 2 and 3. Why are you an artist? What moves you to sell your works? What moved the artists you admire to sell their works?

Selling art is easy if you make it inexpensive enough. If you do that, however, you run the risk of losing, rather than making, money. In addition, if the price is too low, your works may lose credibility as well.

Before we can discuss pricing, we need to have a common understanding of five important concepts: Total Fixed Costs, Average Fixed Cost, Per Unit Variable Costs, Profit, and Income.

- Total Fixed Costs: Those expenses which exist even if we do not create any work. Included under this heading are expenses for: Studio Overhead and Maintenance, Advertising & Promotion, Insurance, Tools, and Vehicles.

- Average Fixed Cost: One arrives at the average of fixed cost which may be assigned to a particular artwork by dividing the total fixed costs for a given time period by the number of artworks produced during that period. If a particular artwork required an unusually long or short period of time to produce, one should make the appropriate adjustments during the pricing process.

- Per Unit Variable Cost: Those non-fixed costs which may be attributed to a specific artwork. Included under this heading are expenses for: Labor, Materials, Packaging, and Delivery.

- Profit: The money one makes *over and above* one's operating costs (Note: since the artist is the producer of the art, his or her personal maintenance must be included in the operating expenses).

- Income: For most artists, income is the profit plus the artist's share of the labor costs. *Note: The discussion of Income will be postponed until section VI: "Making Money."*

About Profit:

One reason for including profit over and above the artist's personal maintenance in the following calculations is that if one does not make a profit one will have only enough money to survive. In order to nurture and grow your career you need to do better than just "break even."

The following pages explore five methods of pricing. Each has its advantages and disadvantages. The pricing method you choose may vary depending on your goals and circumstances. Let's look at what one needs to know in order to price effectively.

Note:
A desktop or hand-held calculator will be useful
in completing the following sections.

3. DETERMINING TOTAL FIXED COSTS

Fixed costs are those expenses which exist even if you do not create any work. Included under this heading are expenses for: Studio Overhead and Maintenance, Advertising & Promotion, Insurance, Tools, and Vehicles. To determine the Total of Fixed Costs choose a time period (a month or a year are usually good) and then enter the costs in the chart below and add them up. The primary purpose of this chart is to make sure you do not ignore one or more costs. Enter amounts only where applicable.

MY FIXED COSTS per (circle one) WEEK MONTH YEAR	
PREMISES COSTS*:	Studio Rent	
	Studio Mortgage	
	Maintenance / Repairs	
	Miscellaneous	
	Other	
	Other	
UTILITY COSTS*:	Heat	
	Electricity	
	Telephone	
	Internet Access	
	Other	
EQUIPMENT COSTS:	Art Tools	
Office Equipment (Computer, Copier, Printer, Scanner, etc.)	
Art Equipment (Etching Press, Darkroom Equipment, etc.)	
	Other	
INSURANCE COSTS:	Insurance on Premises*	
	Insurance on Artwork	
	Insurance on Artist	
	Insurance on Vehicles*	
	Other	
ADVERTISING COSTS:	Business Cards	
	Slides and Photos	
	Website Maintenance	
	Print Advertising	
	Other	
VEHICLE COSTS*:	Business Mileage	
	Maintenance & Repairs	
	Other	
Total of My Fixed Costs per Week Month Year (circle one)	

* Since many artists work in their residences and use their private vehicles for business, the items marked with asterisks may be percentages of costs normally associated with the home.

4. DETERMINING AVERAGE FIXED COST

One arrives at the average of fixed costs which may be assigned to a particular artwork by dividing the total fixed costs for a given time period by the number of artworks produced during that period. If a particular artwork required an unusually long or short period of time to produce, one should make the appropriate adjustments during the pricing process. Use the form below as a template for your calculations.

```
┌─────────────────────────────────────────────────────────────────────┐
│                    AVERAGE FIXED COST FORM                            │
└─────────────────────────────────────────────────────────────────────┘
```

```
┌─────────────────────────────────────────────────────────────────────┐
│                                                                       │
│         Total Fixed Costs (from Section 4)  _____              │
│                                                                       │
│                                             Divided by                │
│                                                                       │
│    Number of artworks produced in selected time period  _____      │
│                                                                       │
│                                               equals                  │
│                                                                       │
│    Average Fixed Cost to be assigned to a particular work*  _____    │
│                                                                       │
│    *Note: The average fixed cost may need to be adjusted if a specific│
│    work takes more or less time to produce than other works made      │
│    during the same period.                                            │
│                                                                       │
└─────────────────────────────────────────────────────────────────────┘
```

It is important to remember that the Average Fixed Cost will decrease as more pieces are produced. This is because the costs of overhead, rent, electricity, phone, etc. remain constant no matter how many pieces are made.

5. DETERMINING PER UNIT VARIABLE COST

Per Unit Variable Cost is the total of the non-fixed costs which may be attributed to a specific artwork. To determine the total of the non-fixed costs which should be attributed to a specific artwork enter each cost in the chart below and add them up. The primary purpose of this chart is to make sure you do not ignore one or more costs. Enter amounts only where applicable.

FORM FOR DETERMINING PER UNIT VARIABLE COST

Title of Artwork: _____

MATERIALS COSTS:	
Canvas	
Paper	
Stretcher Strips	
Paint	
Ink	
Pencil	
Miscellaneous	
Tools (brushes, etc.)	
Other	

PACKAGING (framing?) COSTS:	
Frame	
Glass	
Mat	
Wire, Hardware, etc.	
Other	

SELLING COSTS:	
Travel	
Exhibition Entry Fees	
Gallery Fees	
Meals with Gallery Owners or Clients	
Commission	
Other	
Other	

LABOR COSTS: Me: hourly rate: _____ x _____ (no. of hours) =	
Studio Assistants' Wages (if any)	
Other	

SHIPPING and/or DELIVERY COSTS: Gas & Tolls	
Me: hourly rate: _____ x _____ (no. of hours) =	
UPS or Fedex Charges	
Other	

Per Unit Variable Cost (add up all above)	

> "Beware of little expenses; a small leak will sink a great ship." —*Benjamin Franklin*

Taking a Break

"Life is merely a fraction of a second.
An infinitely small amount of time to fulfill
our desires, our dreams, our passions."
— Paul Gauguin

Unlike Paul Gauguin, who was a successful stockbroker well-versed in economics before he exchanged Paris for Polynesia and painted the glorious paintings of South Pacific life which are so famous today, most artists have little financial training. For many of us, filling out the forms on the preceding pages has been, at best, a difficult task, and, at worst, an unpleasant one. For most of us, taking a break at this point is a good idea.

At times like these I find it useful to imagine that I am in a line which looks like the ticket line at the movies. Not a single-file line like the fire-drill line or the line at the government office, this line is three or four people wide and folks are talking to one another. And as I look around I realize that this line is composed of artists. At the very back of the line (even though this does not make sense to me) is the very first artist, that man or woman who went out on a rainy day, saw his or her footprint in the mud, leaned down and put his or her hand in the mud, and ran back inside and placed his or her hand against the wall of the cave, leaving a muddy handprint there. At the front of the line (near the ticket counter) are some artists whose faces are indistinct, the artists of the future. In between are all the artists who have every lived.

I am happy in this line. I sense that there exists an invisible bond which ties me to the other artists, past, present, and future, with whom I share this line. I believe that they know how I feel when I am creating and that I know how they feel as well. I am thrilled to be an artist.

And as I listen to, and participate in, the conversations that are going on around me, I notice that much of the dialogue is about where to buy supplies at the lowest prices, what galleries take what percentages, how to buy health insurance (remember, I live in the U.S.), the high costs of renting studio space, and other subjects which all have to do with money.

And all this talk about money makes me realize that there is a point to the effort I am putting into "doing" the "hard parts" of this book. The conversations remind me that economics is a part of the life of every artist and I realize that when I have finished the exercises in this book I will find myself able to make money selling my work and thus spend more of my time doing the creative work that I love to do.

6. PRICING METHODS

As previously indicated, five Pricing Methods will be discussed here. Each has its advantages and disadvantages. The pricing method you choose may vary depending on your goals and circumstances. A calculator will help you complete this section.

1. **Variable Cost + Average Fixed Cost + Commission (if any) + Profit = Price**

    This is the easiest of the methods to calculate. Just fill in the blanks and you will arrive at a price for a given work. Because the commission is almost always based on the selling price, it has been separated from the other non-fixed costs in order to simplify the calculations. Note 1: When using this form it will help to find the total of the Non-Fixed Costs first and then perform the rest of the calculations. Note 2: The Total of the Non-Fixed Costs is the same as the Per Unit Variable Cost.

COSTS + COMMISSION + PROFIT PRICING FORM

Title of Artwork: _____

NON-FIXED COSTS		
	Materials Cost	
	Packaging Cost	
	Selling Cost	
	Artist's Labor Cost	
	Other Labor Cost (studio assistant, framer, ?)	
	Shipping and/or Delivery Cost	
Line A	Total Non-Fixed Costs	

Line B	Total Non-Fixed Costs (*Line A*) = Per Unit Variable Cost:	
Line C	Average Fixed Cost (from previous section):	
	PRICE BEFORE COMMISSION AND PROFIT (*sum of lines B & C*)	
	COMMISSION (if any)	
	PROFIT	
	PRICE (sum of preceding three lines)	

2. Competition & Market Factors Determine Price.

Making art is not about competition but selling art can be. *Use the following forms to arrive at a price based on Competition and Market Conditions. Follow the instructions carefully. In Part 1 you should enter a figure on line B or C but not on both.*

COMPETITION & MARKET FACTORS PRICING FORM

Title of Work:
_____

A. Enter Price you would like to get for work
_____

B. If competition is *selling** work of equal quality for more than the price on line A raise your price to exceed theirs & enter the amount here _____

C. If competition is *selling** work of equal quality for less than the price on line A lower your price to equal theirs and enter the amount here _____

---

* The emphasis on *selling* is because one must determine that the competition's works are *selling* at a given price, not just *hanging on the gallery wall* at that price.

Take the price you entered on line B or C and subject it to "profit test" by using the Profit Calculation Form below. When using the Profit Calculation Form, it will help to first find the total of the Non-Fixed Costs and then perform the rest of the calculations.

PROFIT CALCULATION FORM

Title of Artwork: _____

Insert Retail Price of Artwork here (from line B or C of previous form) _____

Subtract Commission to Gallery (if any) - _____

NON-FIXED COSTS		
	Materials Cost	
	Packaging Cost	
	Selling Cost	
	Artist's Labor Cost	
	Other Labor Cost (studio assistant, framer, ?)	
	Shipping and/or Delivery Cost	
Line A	Total Non-Fixed Cost (*enter on line B*)	

Line B   Subtract Per Unit Variable Cost (total of non-fixed costs): - _____

Line C   Subtract Average Fixed Cost (from Section 4, pg. 23): - _____

PROFIT (OR LOSS): _____

If the Profit Calculation Form results in a profit enter your Retail Price here: _____
If the Profit Calculation Form results in a "loss" then you must raise your price and try again.

3. Allowing Career Goals to Determine Price.

Sometimes a museum or other institution will have a limited budget for purchasing art. Perhaps their budget will not be large enough to meet your normal price. You may still wish to sell them the work at a price which fits their budget for reasons such as those which follow:

- On occasion an artist may feel that a sale is so important (as a resume item, for example) that the price is of little consequence. He or she may even be willing to lose money in order to make the sale. In such cases it is important to recognize both the advantages and disadvantages.

- Some Possible Reasons for Lowering Price to further Career Goals include: Getting into Important Collections, Acquiring a New (specific) Client, Acquiring Needed Cash, Completing Newsworthy Sale, Affirming Faith in one's Artwork, Impressing Other Clients, and Ending a "Dry" Spell.

- Some Possible Advantages of Lowering Price to further Career Goals include: Acquiring New Credentials, Generating the Possibility of Future Sales, Increased Prestige, Publicity, Gaining "entry" into a particular Institution, Gallery, or Collection.

- Some Possible Disadvantages of Lowering Price to further Career Goals include: Loss of Income, Cash Loss, Loss of Credibility, Loss of Self-Respect, Discouragement.

Arrive at a price and enter it in the Profit Calculation Form below. Then perform the calculation to determine profit (if any).

PROFIT CALCULATION FORM		
Title of Artwork:		
Insert Retail Price of Artwork here (from line B or C of previous form)		
Subtract Commission to Gallery (if any)	-	
NON-FIXED COSTS Materials Cost		
Packaging Cost		
Selling Cost		
Artist's Labor Cost		
Other Labor Cost (studio assistant, framer, ?)		
Shipping and/or Delivery Cost		
Line A Total Non-Fixed Costs (*enter on line B*)		
Line B Subtract Per Unit Variable Cost (total non-fixed cost):	-	
Line C Subtract Average Fixed Cost (from Section 4, pg. 23):	-	
PROFIT (OR LOSS):		

If the Profit Calculation Form results in a profit enter your Retail Price here: _____
If the Profit Calculation Form results in a "loss" then you will need to decide if the career goals which are the deciding factors in this pricing method are important enough for you to sell the work at a loss.

4. Allowing Career Achievements to Determine Price.

Past glory can sometimes justify a higher price. Some artists have achieved so much and acquired so many credentials that their achievements will justify, in their minds, and the minds of their clients, higher prices for their works.

Some of the achievements which will support raising your prices are Major Solo Gallery Shows, Major Museum Group (or solo) Shows, Articles in Important Publications, Positive Reviews in Newspapers or Art Magazines, Inclusion in Important Public or Private Collections.

Consider the points above. If you feel they apply to you, arrive at a price accordingly. Even if you raise you price significantly, it is still a good idea to subject your price to the "profit test" using the Profit Calculation Form so that you will know what your profit will be .

PROFIT CALCULATION FORM		
Title of Artwork: _____		
Insert Retail Price of Artwork here (from line B or C of previous form)		
Subtract Commission to Gallery (if any)	-	
NON-FIXED COSTS Materials Cost		
Packaging Cost		
Selling Cost		
Artist's Labor Cost		
Other Labor Cost (studio assistant, framer, ?)		
Shipping and/or Delivery Cost		
Line A Total Non-Fixed Cost (*enter on line B*)		
Line B Subtract Per Unit Variable Cost (total non-fixed costs):	-	
Line C Subtract Average Fixed Cost (from Section 4, pg. 23):	-	
PROFIT (OR LOSS):		

Consider the result of the "Profit Test" form and adjust your price if you wish.

5. Allowing Whim to Determine Price.

Many of us are so eager to sell our work that we price it well below what is reasonable. Others put unrealistically high prices on their works. While we are well within our rights to do either, it is worth while asking ourselves whether or not our pricing strategies are helping us to achieve our goals.

You can price your work on whim, but doing so exposes you, the artist, to the risks of losing money, prestige or the respect of others in the arts community.

Random Reflections on Pricing One's Works

If one is selling in a gallery it is important to understand that both you and the gallery have a stake in finding the right price. Imagine a gallery in New York City which pays rent of $10,000 or more per month. If, like many galleries in New York, the gallery's share is 50%, a one-month show must have at least $40,000 dollars worth of artwork on the walls in order to cover rent, telephone, salaries, etc. (*and that's assuming that everything in the show sells!*). It is therefore sometimes customary, when working with galleries, to involve them in the pricing process.

It is easier to publicly raise one's prices than it is to publicly lower them.

If you work with galleries, they will not like it if you price your works elsewhere for less than in their shows. It undermines their credibility.

Larger works almost always are priced higher than smaller ones while the artist is alive. It is only after an artist dies and time has allowed critics, historians, and collectors to examine the relative merits of individual works that the works are judged on their quality rather than their size.

Each artist must make the final decision on pricing for him or her self.

Part V:
Promoting Yourself & Your Work
1. Promotion in General | 2. Believing in Your Work | 3. Promoting Your Work
4. Believing in Yourself | 5. Promoting Yourself | 6. Press Releases
7. Visuals | 8. Press Connections | 9. Non-Print Promotion

1. Promotion in General

No artist starts out well-known. In the visual arts, artists have rarely been "discovered." Almost always the artist's career is the result of some one (often the artist him or her self) bringing the artist and his or her work to the attention of the public.

Some folks recognize the word "promotion" to mean "being put ahead of others" and they find that distasteful. Other folks, believing the word "promotion" implies falseness, cunning, or trickery, close their ears the minute they hear it mentioned. Promotion need not carry these negative implications, especially when that which is being promoted is something you believe in.

Artists have the choice of promoting themselves, their artwork, or both. Picasso, master artist-promoter of the 20th century, promoted himself even more than his art. There are millions of people who recognize "Picasso" as the name of an artist but would not recognize a work by Picasso if they saw one. On the other hand, there are millions of Americans who are familiar with the painting "American Gothic" (the Midwestern couple standing in front of their home with the pitchfork) and do not know the name of the artist who painted it (Grant Wood).

We live in a complex world which few of our ancestors imagined. The worlds of DaVinci, Durer, and Donatello were miniscule compared with ours. Whether we call it promotion, advertising, public relations, or any other term of our choice, if we want our art to find its audience, we are going to have to guide that audience to our art.

2. Believing in Your Work

Believing in your work is important if you are to do a good job promoting it. From the following options select a minimum of five reasons why you believe in your work *(Place checks in at least five of the boxes or write your own reasons on the lines provided, or do both)*:

☐ It is emotional
☐ It is honest
☐ It is satisfying
☐ It is provocative
☐ It is cheerful
☐ It fills a need
☐ It is peaceful

☐ It is heartwarming
☐ It captures the essence of nature
☐ It is technically excellent
☐ It is in harmony with the universe
☐ It comes from deep within me
☐ It makes a statement
☐ It makes people happy

☐ People enjoy it
☐ It is respectable
☐ It is decorative
☐ It is political
☐ It is profound
☐ It is well made
☐ It tells a story

☐ It is symbolic	☐ There is truth in it	☐ It is strong
☐ It is good	☐ There is love in it	☐ It is spiritual
☐ It is humorous	☐ It makes me happy	☐ It is needed
☐ It contains ideas	☐ It is different	☐ It is fun
☐ It communicates	☐ It fills my heart	☐ It is new
☐ It is beautiful	☐ It is exciting	☐ I love it
☐ _____	☐ _____	☐ _____
☐ _____	☐ _____	☐ _____
☐ _____	☐ _____	☐ _____

3. PROMOTING YOUR WORK

While it is possible to pay a professional to promote your work, the thrust of this workbook is on do-it-yourself promotion. It would be nice if your primary gallery (assuming one *is* represented by a gallery) would take on the promotion responsibilities but all too often the reality of the situation is that the gallery is understaffed and the staff is overextended. And, even if your gallery does do some promoting of the artists they represent, their efforts are unlikely to be as focused as your own would be.

Start by taking a look at your work from a promotion point of view. What is interesting, different, or exciting about your work? Reviewing your answers to Part II Section 1 (pg. 13) may be helpful as you fill in the following blanks.

My work is interesting because:

_____

_____

_____

_____

_____

_____

 BUY Art!

My work is different because:

_____

_____

_____

_____

_____

_____

_____

_____

My work is exciting because:

_____

_____

_____

_____

_____

_____

_____

_____

What you have written above, along with some "plain facts" and a photograph of your work, will be more than sufficient for a press release* about your work and/or yourself. More about that later...

*Sample Press Releases can be found in the Appendix

4. BELIEVING IN YOURSELF

In the same way that believing in your work is important if you are to do a good job promoting it, believing in your self is important if you want to do a good job of promoting yourself. From the following options select a minimum of ten things which you believe to be true about yourself *(Place checks in at least ten of the boxes, write your own reasons on the lines provided, or do both. Select as many as you wish).*

☐ I am unique	☐ I trust others	☐ I like myself
☐ I care about my work	☐ I seek truth	☐ I am loving
☐ I do good work	☐ I am patient	☐ I am innovative
☐ I am thoughtful	☐ I believe in God	☐ I am different
☐ I am cheerful	☐ I do not believe in God	☐ I learn easily
☐ I respect others	☐ I am a spiritual person	☐ I have talent
☐ I am focused	☐ I am thoughtful	☐ I am pragmatic
☐ I am free-spirited	☐ I am a good planner	☐ I am spontaneous
☐ I am strong	☐ I trust my emotions	☐ I am gifted
☐ I wish no ill to anyone	☐ I am non-judgmental	☐ I am kind
☐ I am intelligent	☐ I can do almost anything	☐ I am exciting
☐ I am willing to learn	☐ I put my heart into my work	☐ I am sensitive
☐ I am funny	☐ I have a positive attitude	☐ I am insightful
☐ I am loving	☐ I am centered	☐ I am articulate
☐ I am multi-talented	☐ I am a realist	☐ I am caring
☐ I like to play	☐ I am hard-working	☐ I am helpful
☐ I am fun-loving	☐ I am respectable	☐ I am candid
☐ I am fair	☐ I am delightfully not-respectable	☐ I am optimistic
☐ I like to work	☐ I am open-minded	☐ I am careful
☐ I am brave	☐ I have experienced a lot	☐ I am special
☐ I am energetic	☐ I am comfortable with myself	☐ I am considerate
☐ I am friendly	☐ I am comfortable with others	☐ I am resolute
☐ I am smart	☐ I seek new experiences	☐ I am honest
☐ I am courageous	☐ I am well organized	☐ _____
☐ I am gentle	☐ I am delightfully disorganized	☐ _____
☐ _____	☐ _____	☐ _____
☐ _____	☐ _____	☐ _____

5. PROMOTING YOURSELF

Promotion in the art world is as much about promoting yourself as it is about promoting your work. This is the time to put aside modesty and self esteem issues and do the best job you can.

Take a look at yourself from a promotion point of view. What is interesting, different, or exciting about you?

I am interesting because:

....

....

....

....

....

....

....

....

I am different because:

....

....

....

....

....

....

....

....

....

I am exciting because:

....

....

....

....

....

....

....

....

What you have written above, along with some "plain facts" and a photograph (of yourself and/or your work) will be more than sufficient for a press release* about your work and/or yourself.

*Sample Press Releases can be found in the Appendix

6. PRESS RELEASES

What are the possible reasons for sending out a press release about your work?
Check those which might apply to your work or make up your own.

☐ Work to be Displayed at _____

☐ Work to be Exhibited at _____

☐ Work Subject of New Website _____

☐ Work Wins Award at _____

☐ Work Acquired by Famous Collector

☐ Work Acquired by _____ Collection

☐ Work in Group Exhibition at _____

☐ Work Commissioned by _____

☐ Work represents New Technique _____

☐ Work reproduced in Book _____

☐ Work Found Offensive by _____

☐ Subject Matter of Work Interesting to Public

☐ _____

☐ _____

What "plain facts" will you need? *Fill in as many of the blanks as you can.*

Title of Work: _____

Medium: _____

Date Completed (if recent): _____

Name of Artist (yourself): _____

Description of Subject Matter: _____

_____

When (date of event or occurrence): _____

Where (location of event or occurrence): _____

Who (other than yourself) is involved: (Museum, Art Center, Collection, Gallery, their personnel

etc.): _____

Why (if relevant): _____

*For a sample press releases see the Appendix to this workbook.

7. VISUALS

Visual art is best promoted visually. The more people who see your work, and the more *often* they see it, the more they will recognize it. Some of the common ways of getting the public to see your work, or pictures of your work, are listed below. Note that having a picture of yourself appear in a print or online publication or other visual medium can often be as important as having a picture of your work appear there.

Check the box in the first column if you already use a particular approach. Check the box in the second column if you do not use a particular approach but would like to use it in the future. Make up your own approaches in the blanks provided.

	Already Use	Use in Future
Exhibiting the work itself	☐	☐
Slides	☐	☐
Exhibition announcements	☐	☐
Newspaper articles	☐	☐
Magazine articles	☐	☐
Promotional brochures	☐	☐
Reproductions in books about art	☐	☐
Books specifically about your work	☐	☐
Posters	☐	☐
The Internet	☐	☐
Catalogs	☐	☐
Greeting cards	☐	☐
Postcards	☐	☐
Magazine ads	☐	☐
Writing articles for publications	☐	☐
Getting your art on book covers	☐	☐
Getting listed in art directories	☐	☐
Television	☐	☐
Other: _____	☐	☐
Other: _____	☐	☐
Other: _____	☐	☐
Other: _____	☐	☐

8. MEDIA CONNECTIONS

Often the most direct route to successful media promotion is through personal connections. If you know someone who works at a TV station, newspaper or magazine your chances of getting into that publication increase dramatically. Often knowing "someone who knows someone" will help as well.

List below those people who might be able to help you with your promotional efforts. Anyone who works in the media or has contacts in the media should be listed here. If there are not enough lines, use the margins of the paper. If you don't fill the lines it's OK. You can always add more names later.

Name of Person	Publication, Phone Number & E-mail

9. Non- Print Promotion

Among the non-print possibilities for promoting yourself and your work are:

☐ Broadcast Media (Radio and TV)
☐ The Internet
☐ Donations of Art for Fundraising Purposes
☐ Donations of Art to Public Institutions
☐ Lending Art for Public Display
☐ "Crazy" Attention-getting Stunts (make sure they are safe and legal)
☐ "Outrageous" Attention-getting Activities or Statements (make sure they are safe and legal)
☐ Your Own Promotional Video

Check those which appeal to you.

Reflections on Old Sayings and Being Fair

"...money is the root of all evil."
— I Timothy 6:10

Some of us, hearing the saying that "money is the root of all evil," have responded by doing our best to minimize our involvement with money. This is dangerous for artists. Sadly, most of us do not know that the quote, in this, its popular form, is abbreviated. This shortening of the quote makes it at least misleading and at most incorrect. A more complete version of the words of Paul as they appear in I Timothy 6:10 reads "the *love of money* is the root of all evil." It is *love* which is the operator in this phrase and specifically *the love of money*. *Money* alone is not evil, nor is it the root of evil.

We receive many anti-money messages from old sayings. "He who multiplies riches, multiplies cares" *(Benjamin Franklin)*, "It is easier for a camel to go through the eye of a needle than for a rich man to enter the kingdom of God" *(Mark 10:25)*, and "Neither a borrower nor a lender be" *(Polonius in Hamlet, William Shakespeare)* are just a few of them.

In the face of such messages, how are we to feel good about our efforts to obtain money and the benefits that it provides? Perhaps the quotes below and on the next page will help:

"Money answereth all things." — *Ecclesiastes 10:19*

"Lack of money is the root of all evil." — *George Bernard Shaw (also attributed to Mark Twain)*

"Wealth is well known to be a great comforter." — *Plato*

"Capital as such is not evil; it is its wrong use that is evil. Capital in some form
or other will always be needed." — *Gandhi*

"On the whole, money does artists much more good than harm. The idea that one benefits from
cold water, crusts and debt collectors is now almost extinct, like belief in the
reformatory power of flogging." — *Robert Hughes*

"When I was young I used to think that money was the most important thing in life;
now that I am old, I know it is." — *Oscar Wilde*

"A large income is the best recipe for happiness I ever heard of." — *Jane Austen*

"I'd like to live like a poor man with lots of money." — *Pablo Picasso*

"Riches cover a multitude of woes." — *Menander*

"If money be not thy servant, it will be thy master." — *Francis Bacon*

"A woman must have money and room of her own if she is to write fiction" — *Virginia Wolfe*

"It is a kind of spiritual snobbery that makes people think they can be
happy without money." — *Albert Camus*

"So you think that money is the root of all evil.
Have you ever asked what is the root of all money?"— *Ayn Rand*

"Poverty is a blessing hated by all men." — *Italian Proverb*

"Those who have some means think that the most important thing in the world is love.
The poor know that it is money" — *Gerald Brenan*

"Money, if it does not bring you happiness, will at least help you be miserable in comfort."
— *Helen Gurley Brown*

"People who say that money is the root of all evil don't have any" — *Anonymous*

"Money is a kind of poetry." — *Wallace Stevens*

"Money, which represents the prose of life, and which is hardly spoken of in parlors without
an apology, is, in its effects and laws, as beautiful as roses." — *Ralph Waldo Emerson*

"Liking money like I like it, is nothing less than mysticism." — *Salvador Dalí*

"Money is better than poverty, if only for financial reasons." — *Woody Allen*

Once, while trying to sort out my own personal relationship with money, I told my friend Allison
that I thought that "in the best of all possible worlds all people would have the same amount of
money." Allison responded with this guided image: "Imagine that you are walking west on 42nd
street in New York City. Imagine you are on the block between 5th and 6th Avenues. You see a
beggar with a styrofoam cup and a sign that says "Homeless with Five Children." You look in your
pocket and find that you have one hundred dollars. In accordance with your belief in equality, you
put fifty dollars in the beggar's cup and keep fifty dollars for yourself. You go on your way feeling
good. But the block between 5th and 6th Avenues is a long block and pretty soon you come to
another beggar with a styrofoam cup and a sign that says "Please Help A Veteran." Again you are
moved to charity so you put half of your money, twenty-five dollars this time, in the beggar's cup.
But think about it," said Allison, "now the first beggar has fifty dollars and you only have twenty-
five. Your single-handed effort to create economic equality in the world, no matter how well-
intentioned, did not work. And it cannot work unless you, the benefactor, have unlimited wealth."

I have taken Allison's words to heart. I am fair in my financial dealings, but always mindful that
being fair means being fair to *myself* as well as to *others*.

PART VI
MAKING MONEY
1. Art as Product / 2. Pricing and Income

For some of us, making money is not the primary motive for marketing our work. That may, in fact, be true for most of us. But even if it is not our primary motive, making money is important to many of us. This section will allow you to evaluate your marketing plan's potential for economic success.

1. ART AS PRODUCT

To most artists, the *process* of making art is more important than the *product* which results. When we teach we are selling the process. But when we sell our artwork we are selling product. Development of a successful Marketing & Action Plan requires that each of us take a financial look at his or her artwork. Answering the following questions will help. One of the goals of these questions is to help you find out how much money you can make at your current price level and rate of production.

As you answer the questions, please check the box that most correctly completes the sentence. Use the margins for computation if necessary.

1. The average price of a piece of my work is: $ _____ .

2. I produce ☐ a large amount ☐ a medium amount ☐ a small amount of art.

3. On the average, it takes me _____ hours to produce a work of art.

4. My time is worth $ _____ per hour.

5. I have on hand ☐ a large amount ☐ a medium amount ☐ a small amount of art.

6. When I sell a piece of art work directly to a retail customer
   ☐ 20% ☐ 30% ☐ 40% ☐ 50% ☐ 60% ☐ 70% ☐ more than 70% ☐ I don't know
   of the sale price is profit.

7. When I sell a piece of art work through a gallery
   ☐ 20% ☐ 30% ☐ 40% ☐ 50% ☐ 60% ☐ 70% ☐ more than 70% ☐ I don't know
   of the sale price is profit.

8. My estimated profit, in dollars, on an average piece of my art is: $ _____
   Base your answer on the calculations you did in Part IV and/or on your answers to questions 6 and 7 above.

There will more questions, but it will help to focus, for a few moments, on *income*. In the real world of the artist, it is *income* which pays the rent, buys groceries and art supplies, etc.

Income and Profit are not the same. For most artists, income is the profit <u>plus</u> the artist's share of the labor costs. While the artist never writes a check for his or her labor costs, they are costs just the same. Your labor costs must, therefore, be factored into the price of your work. Since the amount of work you can make is limited, it is important to look at pricing, production, and desired income.

ART AS PRODUCT (CONTINUED)

Income: *Complete the form below to determine the average income you receive (or hope to receive) per piece of artwork sold.*

AVERAGE INCOME PER ARTWORK

What my time is worth per hour (from Question 4 above) $ _____

Multiplied by

Number of hours required to make average artwork (from Question 3 above)

equals

Average artists' labor costs per artwork $ _____

plus

Profit per artwork $ _____

equals

Average income per artwork $ _____

9. My goal is to earn $ _____ *(desired income)* per year through the sale of my artwork.

Using the form below, determine how much artwork you will have to sell to reach your goal.

REQUIRED VOLUME OF ARTWORK

Amount I wish to earn each year through sales of my work (from Question 9) $ _____

divided by

Average Income per artwork (from form above) $ _____

equals

Number of Artworks which need to be sold each year to reach my goal _____

10. I currently make ☐ 50 ☐ 75 ☐ 100 ☐ 150 ☐ 200 ☐ 250 ☐ 300 ☐ 400 ☐ 500 ☐ 750 ☐ 1000 ☐ _____ pieces of art per year.

11. If I sell all the art work I currently make in a year at my current prices I would earn $ _____ per year. *Multiply the number of pieces you make by the average income per artwork from the chart above.*

12. At my current prices I will have to sell
☐ 50 ☐ 75 ☐ 100 ☐ 150 ☐ 200 ☐ 250 ☐ 300 ☐ 400 ☐ 500 ☐ 750 ☐ 1000
☐ _____ pieces of art per year in order to reach my goal.

13. I am capable of making ☐ 50 ☐ 100 ☐ 250 ☐ 500 ☐ 750 ☐ 1000 ☐ _____ pieces of art per year.

Important Note: The artist whose answer to number 12 is greater than his or her answer to number 13 will need to increase production or raise his or her prices in order to reach his or her goal.

2. PRICING AND INCOME

Artists' incomes vary widely. The following charts will help you to understand the relationship between pricing and income. Comparing the results of these four scenarios will help establish the direction of your Marketing/Action Plan. When filling out the following charts use round numbers as it makes both the calculation, and the comparison of the results, easier.

Enter a price in Chart 1 which you know will result in a profit.

Chart 1 – AVERAGE OR HYPOTHETICAL SALE - Your Price	
Directly to Customer	**Through Gallery**
Insert Retail Price of Artwork here _____	and here _____
Subtract Commission to Gallery _*0*_	Subtract Commission to Gallery _____
Subtract Average Fixed Cost (from form in Part IV Section 4, pg. 23) _____	Subtract Average Fixed Cost (from form in Part IV Section 4, pg. 23) _____
Subtract Per Unit Variable Costs (from form in Part IV Section 5, pg. 24) _____	Subtract Per Unit Variable Costs (from form in Part IV Section 5, pg. 24) _____
Add Artist's share of Labor Costs (from form in Part IV Section 5, pg. 24) _____	Add Artist's share of Labor Costs (from form in Part IV Section 5, pg. 24) _____
Income 1 A _____	Income 1 B _____

When filling out Chart #2 below, increase the retail price established on Chart #1. Note that while an increase in price changes the gallery's commission, it does not change the other costs.

Chart 2 – AVERAGE OR HYPOTHETICAL SALE AT INCREASED PRICE	
Directly to Customer	**Through Gallery**
Insert Retail Price of Artwork here _____	and here _____
Subtract Commission to Gallery _*0*_	Subtract Commission to Gallery _____
Subtract Average Fixed Cost (from form in Part IV Section 4, pg. 23) _____	Subtract Average Fixed Cost (from form in Part IV Section 4, pg. 23) _____
Subtract Per Unit Variable Costs (from form in Part IV Section 5, pg. 24) _____	Subtract Per Unit Variable Costs (from form in Part IV Section 5, pg. 24) _____
Add Artist's share of Labor Costs (from form in Part IV Section 5, pg. 24) _____	Add Artist's share of Labor Costs (from form in Part IV Section 5, pg. 24) _____
Income 2 A _____	Income 2 B _____

After you have finished Charts 1 and 2 compare the income scenarios using Charts 3 and 4 on the next page.

2. PRICING AND INCOME (CONTINUED)

Chart 3 – RETAIL PRICE COMPARISON CHART	
Directly to Customer	**Through Gallery**
Retail Price from Chart 2 _____	Retail Price from Chart 2 _____
Subtract Retail Price from Chart 1 _____	Subtract Retail Price from Chart 1 _____
Equals: _____	Equals: _____
Divided by Retail Price from Chart 1 _____	Divided by Retail Price from Chart 1 _____
Equals Percentage Increase in Price (3A) _____	Equals Percentage Increase in Price (3B) _____

Chart 4 – INCOME COMPARISON CHART	
Directly to Customer	**Through Gallery**
Income from Chart 2 (2A) _____	Income from Chart 2 (2B) _____
Subtract Income from Chart 1 (1A) _____	Subtract Income from Chart 1 (1B) _____
Equals: _____	Equals: _____
Divided by Income from Chart 1 (1A) _____	Divided by Income from Chart 1 (1B) _____
Equals Percentage Increase in Income (4A) _____	Equals Percentage Increase in Income (4B) _____

Use the charts above to compare 4A with 3A and 4B with 3B. Which is greater? Complete the following statements by checking one box in each statement.

1. The percentage increase in income is *(check one)* ☐ greater than ☐ less than ☐ equal to the percentage increase in the retail price in direct sales.

2. The percentage increase in income is *(check one)* ☐ greater than ☐ less than ☐ equal to the percentage increase in the retail price in gallery sales.

If you checked anything other than "greater than" you have made a mistake in your calculations. The percentage of increase in income will always be greater than the percentage of increase in the retail price.

PART VII
PERSONAL / BUSINESS GOALS
1. Determining Goals

In Part I Section 3 of this workbook under the heading "What Does Success Look Like?" you took a brief look at goals. At this time it will be useful to separate your goals into personal goals or business goals. Sometimes it is not clear which category a goal belongs in. There is no rule which says a goal cannot be both a *personal* goal and a *business* goal.

Generally speaking, short term goals are those which will be realized within the next year and long term goals are those which will be realized more than a year into the future.

1. DETERMINING GOALS

Use the forms on the next two pages to write down your goals.

First, review the goal you wrote at the end of Part I (on page 12 - the one identified as "My Main Goal"). Is it a personal goal or a business goal? Is it a short-term goal or a long-term goal? If it is a long term goal write it at the top of the appropriate column of the Long Term Goal form. If it is a short term goal write it at the top of the appropriate column of the Short Term Goal form. Then fill in the rest of the forms with information from Part I Section 3 and anything you would like to add now.

There is no rule which says a goal cannot be both a personal *goal and a* business *goal.*

Goals change. Additional copies of these forms will be found in the Appendix and are marked "Master for Photocopying." They may be photocopied as often as you like for future use.

The Action Plan Forms in the next section will help you achieve these goals.

LONG TERM GOALS

PERSONAL	BUSINESS

SHORT TERM GOALS

PERSONAL	BUSINESS

PART VIII
ACTION PLAN FORMS
1. Instructions | 2. Form For Short Term Goals
3. Form for Long Term Goals

1. INSTRUCTIONS

This section contains Action Plan Forms for Short and Long Term Goals. One copy of each form is for immediate practice. Additional copies of these forms may be found in the Appendix and are marked "Master for Photocopying." They may be photocopied as often as you like for future use.

Here are the instructions for using the forms:

1. STATE GOAL: State your objective as clearly and concisely as possible. If, especially in the case of short-term goals, the objective seems too complex, divide it into two or more objectives.

2. ASSESS CURRENT SITUATION: Define the Strengths and Weaknesses of the Current Situation. These include not only your personal strengths and weaknesses but also the strengths and weaknesses of the environment in which the action will take place. Define the Benefits and Risks which may result from your efforts to achieve the goal.

Example: Goal: INCREASE ART SALES

Strengths	Weaknesses	Benefits	Risks
MY HIGH QUALITY ART GOOD CONNECTIONS AWARDS STRONG MARKET FOR MY KIND OF ART FRESHNESS OF WORK MY COMMITMENT MY ENERGY	NO NAME RECOGNITION INEXPERIENCE LITTLE INTEREST IN ART IN MY REGION DISTANCE TO ART CENTERS	INCREASE IN INCOME PERSONAL SATISFACTION POSSIBILITIES FOR FUTURE SUPPORT MY ART "HABIT"	DISAPPOINTMENT WASTE TIME & MONEY LOSS OF RESPECT FROM FAMILY

3. BRAINSTORM APPROPRIATE ACTIONS: Write down possible actions that may help to achieve your goal. Extend onto another sheet of paper if necessary.

4. PRIORITIZE ACTIONS: Decide which of the actions you have brainstormed should come first and which should follow. Decide which actions are essential and which may be abandoned.

5. INSERT DATE GOAL IS TO BE REACHED: Set a "target date" for achieving your goal.

6. CREATE A TIME LINE FOR ACTIONS: Be as specific as possible about what actions will help you achieve your goal, when they should be undertaken, and by what time they should be completed. If other people are involved, define who they are and enter their contact information in the action boxes. Check the final box when an action has been completed.

7. INSERT DATE GOAL IS ACHIEVED: When goal is achieved, fill in this blank.

OTHER: It is a good idea, after a goal has been achieved, to write down what you learned during the process of achieving that goal. The back of the Action Planning Form is a good place to do this.

Action Plan Form for Short Term Goals
(Practice Copy)
Review Instructions Before Using

1. STATE GOAL: _____

2. ASSESS CURRENT SITUATION:

Strengths	Weaknesses	Benefits	Risks

3. BRAINSTORM APPROPRIATE ACTIONS (use this space):

4. PRIORITIZE ACTIONS: Write numbers next to the actions above

5. INSERT DATE GOAL IS TO BE REACHED ("target" date):_____

6. CREATE TIME LINE FOR ACTIONS:

Begin	Action	Complete by	Check when Done

7. INSERT DATE GOAL IS ACHIEVED:_____

Action Plan Form for Long Term Goals
(Practice Copy)
Review Instructions Before Using

1. STATE GOAL: _____

2. ASSESS CURRENT SITUATION:

Strengths	Weaknesses	Benefits	Risks

3. BRAINSTORM APPROPRIATE ACTIONS. <u>INCLUDE SHORT TERM GOALS AS ACTIONS</u> (use this space):

4. PRIORITIZE ACTIONS: Write numbers next to the actions above

5. INSERT DATE GOAL IS TO BE REACHED ("target" date):_____

6. CREATE TIME LINE FOR ACTIONS:

Begin	Action	Complete by	Check when Done

7. INSERT DATE GOAL IS ACHIEVED:_____

PART IX
MAKING IT HAPPEN –
IMPLEMENTING THE ACTION PLAN
1. Dividing Your Time | 2. Creative Time | 3. Scheduling
4. Using the Forms | 4. Reviewing Achievements | 5. Revising Goals
6. Celebrating Successes

1. DIVIDING YOUR TIME

As artists, our profession is intricately and inextricably entwined with almost all aspects of our personal lives. It is useful to think about our activities as being divided into three categories: Creative Activities, Marketing Activities, and Personal/Non-Art Activities.

Use the forms below and on the next page to decide which of these three categories your daily activities belong in.

Check the appropriate spaces below. It is possible that some activities will belong in more than one category. The blank lines at the end of the form are for you to insert activities which are not listed.

Activity	Creative Activities	Marketing Activities	Personal / Non-Art Activities
Answering E-mail			
Answering Phone Calls			
Bookkeeping			
Buying Supplies			
Caring for Others			
Cleaning Studio			
Cleaning House			
Cooking			
Correspondence			
Day-Dreaming			
Doing Laundry			
Dreaming			
Delivering Art			
Eating			
Exercising			
Experimenting			
Framing			
Imagining			
Looking at Art			

Activity	Creative Activities	Marketing Activities	Personal / Non-Art Activities
Looking for Things			
Maintaining Mailing List			
Making Art			
Making Money			
Making Phone Calls			
Meeting Clients			
Meeting Family Obligations			
Meeting Social Obligations			
Other Work			
Playing			
Playing Sports			
Practicing			
Reading			
Repairing Things			
Sleeping			
Shipping			
Staring into Space			
Surfing the Internet			
Studying			
Talking			
Thinking			
Traveling			
Visiting Galleries			
Visiting Museums			
Visiting Friends			
Wasting Time			
Working on the Computer			

Now decide what percentage of your time you wish to devote to each of these categories?
Budget your time on a weekly basis. The chart at the right will help you answer the questions.

	Hours	% of Week
	5 hours =	3%
	10 hours =	6%
	20 hours =	12%
	40 hours =	24%
	50 hours =	30%

A. I wish to devote _____% of my time to Creative Activities

B. I wish to devote _____% of my time to Marketing Activities

C. I wish to devote _____% of my time to Personal / Non-Art Activities

2. CREATIVE TIME

Many of us find that we are most creative at a particular time of the day, week, or year. We may also find that creativity is easiest for us following specific other activities like exercise, conversation, or meditation. *Review the following options and check those which apply to you. Use the blank space for your own additions.*

I am most creative:

☐ In the Early Morning   ☐ After Exercise   ☐ When My Chores are Done

☐ In the Morning   ☐ After Conversation   ☐ At Home

☐ At Midday   ☐ After Meditation   ☐ Away from Home

☐ In the Afternoon   ☐ Before I Eat   ☐ In the Summer

☐ In the Late Afternoon   ☐ After I Eat   ☐ In the Winter

☐ In the Early Evening   ☐ When I am with Others   ☐ In the Spring

☐ In the Evening   ☐ When I am Alone   ☐ In the Fall

☐ At Night   ☐ On Weekends   ☐ _____

☐ Late at Night   ☐ When I have a Deadline   ☐ _____

☐ In the Middle of the Night   ☐ When I have Free Time   ☐ _____

☐ After I've had my Coffee   ☐ When I am Relaxed   ☐ _____

3. SCHEDULING

Establishing a schedule can help you implement your action plan. Review your answers to the previous two sections and create a schedule for yourself on the Daily Schedule Forms on the next two pages. This schedule need not be "written in stone." As your priorities change, your schedule may change as well. Blank Daily Schedule Forms which you may photocopy as often as you wish for future use are included in the Appendix.

Important Note

The Daily Schedule Forms include a column called "Flex Time." This is exactly what it sounds like — time which you choose not to assign to a particular kind of activity so you can build some flexibility into your schedule.

Some things you may want to take into consideration as you create your schedule:

- Have you scheduled enough time for eating and sleeping?

- Can you be creative in short periods of time or do you need a large block of time for creative activity? If so, what does "large" mean to you?

- If you need to be alone for creative activity, how will that affect your schedule?

- Do you need help with any of your activities? Help may be harder to find at 3 AM than at 3 PM.

- If you must travel from your home to your studio, have you allowed enough time?

- Do any of your activities have the potential for disturbing others (by making noise, for example)? If so, have you scheduled them properly?

- How do (or did) your role models schedule their time? Would their schedule work for you? If not, how would you need to change it?

Suggestion: When using the Daily Schedule Forms it may be helpful to first divide your day into Creative Activities, Marketing Activities, Personal / Non-Art Activities, and Flex Time in accordance with the percentages you established in the previous section, and then add specific activities in the spaces provided.

> "If you fail to plan, you plan to fail"
> — *Old Saying*

DAILY SCHEDULE FORM - DAYTIME

TIME	Creative Activities	Marketing Activities	Personal / Non-Art Activities	Flex Time	SPECIFIC ACTIVITY
6:00					
6:30					
7:00					
7:30					
8:00					
8:30					
9:00					
9:30					
10:00					
10:30					
11:00					
11:30					
Noon					
12:30					
1:00					
1:30					
2:00					
2:30					
3:00					
3:30					
4:00					
4:30					
5:00					
5:30					

Daily Schedule Form - Nighttime

Time	Creative Activities	Marketing Activities	Personal / Non-Art Activities	Flex Time	Specific Activity
6:00					
6:30					
7:00					
7:30					
8:00					
8:30					
9:00					
9:30					
10:00					
10:30					
11:00					
11:30					
Midnight					
12:30					
1:00					
1:30					
2:00					
2:30					
3:00					
3:30					
4:00					
4:30					
5:00					
5:30					

4. USING THE FORMS

You have done a lot of work in this book. It is the author's intention that your efforts be of benefit to you on an ongoing basis. The exercises and forms in this book have been created to guide you through the process of learning how to sell your art and how to make money doing it. They can also help you make both these things happen.

If you have ample space, assign a wall, or part of a wall, to your Marketing and Action Plan. Post copies of your Short Term Goal Forms, Long Term Goal Forms, Action Plan Forms, and Daily Schedule Forms where you can see them and consider them every day. Add new forms when needed and file those you remove from the wall in a notebook (a three-ring binder works well) for review at a later time.

If you do not have enough wall space, you will need to use two notebooks. Place copies of your "active" forms in the first notebook. Use dividers to separate Short Term Goals, Long Term Goals, Action Plan Forms, and Daily Schedule Forms. Then, make a habit of considering the contents of this notebook at the same time every day (put it on your schedule). Again, add new forms when needed and file those you remove from your "active" notebook in the second notebook for review at a later time.

5. REVIEWING YOUR ACHIEVEMENTS

Often, especially for those of us who find our studios lonely, it is difficult to remember that our art really is making a difference in our lives and in the lives of others. At times like that, it is very helpful to look at what you have achieved. The forms you have filled out, including the ones which you have already filed, can help you review your achievements.

This review process is often the source of new energy and insights. It can also prompt you to revise your goals.

6. REVISING YOUR GOALS

Sometimes you outgrow your old goals. Sometimes old goals will not provide you with the new opportunities you seek. Sometimes changes in the art world make your old goals invalid. Sometimes changes in your personal life require you to set new goals.

Whatever the reason, periodically revising your goals is important to career development. Every six months, decide what old goals need to be changed or discarded and what new goals need to be established. In the case of new goals, create new Long or Short-Term Goal Forms.

6. <u>CELEBRATING YOUR SUCCESSES</u>

Whether they are big or small, real or symbolic, it is important to celebrate your successes. Achieving a goal indicates that you have worked hard and/or well. You deserve to be rewarded for your efforts. Sometimes the rewards come from others; for example, when you are given a prize at a juried exhibition, or receive a letter of thanks from a school you have visited. Most of the time, however, you will have to reward yourself.

Refer back to Part I, Section 3 (pg. 11) "What does Success Look Like for Each of Us" and review your answers. What kind of successes do you believe are worth celebrating? Consider adding some of the following to your "success list."

Make First Sale	Find New Gallery	Establish New "Personal Best" Price
Make 100th Sale	Receive Commission	Work Acquired by Museum
Make 1000th Sale	Your Art Reviewed	Work Acquired by Important Collector
Accepted in Juried Show	Build New Website	Picture of Work in Art Book
Accepted in Group Show	Have Solo Show	Article in Magazine
Win Award	Enlarge Studio	Learn New Technique

Whenever you have a success, commemorate it in some tangible way. Find your own way to celebrate what you have achieved.

Here are some possibilities:

Buy New Paint Brushes	Take a Vacation	Treat Yourself to a Massage
Have Dinner Out	Visit a Museum	Throw a Party for Your Friends
Take a Day Off	Visit the Art Store	Take a Hike in the Woods
Put Money in the Bank	Buy New Clothes	Get Away for the Weekend
Go Horseback Riding	Buy an Art Book	Buy Something for Your Spouse or Kids
Go Sailing	Write a Poem	Buy Someone Else's Art
Give Yourself Flowers	Go to the Theater	Pat Yourself on the Back
Go for a Walk	Call a Friend	Contemplate Your Success
Go to the Gym	Buy A New Hat	Share the News with Your Family
Make More Art	Go Dancing	Write in Your Journal

PART X
A FEW FINAL THOUGHTS

"When bankers get together for dinner, they discuss art.
When artists get together for dinner, they discuss money."
— Oscar Wilde

Reaching this point means you have done some difficult work. Difficult because filling in forms is as hard for most artists as coloring within the lines. Difficult because the process of working through this book often reveals some pretty harsh realities about the profession we have chosen.

The economics of art are unique. Most of us are not prompted to make art by dreams of economic gain. For most of us, the price of a work of art does not represent its value.

Like any large corporation, an artist develops new ideas, purchases raw materials, manufactures a product, and sells that product. The corporation has separate divisions for each of these functions, but we have only ourselves. We artists wear all the hats: CEO, Comptroller, Accountant, Designer, Engineer, Production Manager, Tool and Die Maker, Assembly Line Worker, Finisher, Director of Marketing and Sales, and Delivery Driver.

We, however, are more than one-person corporations. We are thinking, feeling, striving human beings. Unlike the corporation, we are not beholden to our shareholders and the "bottom line" is not our holy grail. Indeed, for many of us, it is this very lack of indebtedness which has prompted us to become artists.

Why, then, have we chosen to put energy into developing a Marketing/Action Plan to sell our art?

Clearly the answers to this question are as varied and unique as the individual artists for whom this book was written, but we do have much in common. We believe in our work. We believe in its audience. We believe in the process of making art. We know that we are not the first artists to find the economics of our profession challenging, and we know we will not be the last. We know that *selling our work* will provide us with the *greatest opportunity* to *make more art*.

It is not about style. If Andrew Wyeth's realistic paintings are worth millions and Jackson Pollack's abstract paintings are worth millions, then it stands to reason that almost anything in between could be worth millions as well.

Role models are important. Despite the durability of the "starving artist" myth, many artists have supported themselves (and often their families) by selling their art. It may be useful to list some of them here (without prejudice for or against, or judgment of, their talent or style): Picasso, Georgia O'Keefe, Alexander Calder, Artemesia Gentileschi, Miro, El Greco, Thomas Kincaid, Michaelangelo, Piranesi, Mary Cassat, Canaletto, Andrew Wyeth, Nam June Paik, Bev Dolittle, Salvador Dali, Albrecht Durer, Morris Katz, Stuart Davis, Thomas Gainsborough, Fritz Eichenberg, Gordon Grant, John Sloan, John Stobart, Richard Serra, Lynd Ward, Grace Albee, William Hogarth, Giorgio Morandi, Piet Mondrian, Francis Bacon, Thomas Hart Benton, John Taylor Arms, Will Barnet, Chuck Close, Isabel Bishop, Edward Hopper, Judy Chicago, Raphael Soyer, Jean-Michel Basquiat, Stow Wegenroth, Kerr Eby, Wanda Gag, Grant Wood, Joseph Pennell, Richard Diebenkorn, Alberto Giacometti, Lyonel Feininger, Richard Estes, Antoine Watteau, George "Pop" Hart, Andy Warhol, Julian Schnabel, Peter Max, Jacob van Ruisdael, Mark Rothko, Auguste Rodin, Lucian Freud, Gerhard Richter, Sir Joshua Reynolds, Pierre Auguste Renoir, Robert Motherwell, Henri Matisse, Man Ray, Donald Judd, Ingres, Hans Holbein, Joan Mitchell, Andy Goldsworthy, Helen Frankenthaler, Jean Dubuffet, Christo and Jeanne-Claude, Joseph Beuys, Joseph Albers, Sol LeWitt, Niki De Saint Phalle, Ed Ruscha, Maurice Prendergast, Claes Oldenburg, Franz Kline, Aristide Maillol, Hiroshige, René Magritte, Roy Lichtenstein, and Barbara Kruger.

These are just some of the better-known economically "successful" artists of past and present times. There are a multitude more, both living and dead, whose names are known only to a few. You do not need to be world-famous to make a living as an artist. You only need enough customers to support yourself. And there is a far greater demand for art than the few artists above can possibly satisfy.

So...

Make your art, identify your target market, price your art so that it will support you and grow your career, promote your art and yourself, and sell your art to the customers in your market.

And remember two things:

- Those who succeed are those who are willing to risk failure.

- No one deserves success more than you do.

APPENDIX

Short Term Goal Form (for Reproduction)
Review Instructions Before Using

SHORT TERM GOALS	
PERSONAL	**BUSINESS**

Long Term Goal Form (for Reproduction)
Review Instructions Before Using

LONG TERM GOALS	
PERSONAL	BUSINESS

Action Plan Form for Short Term Goals (for Reproduction)

Review Instructions Before Using

1. STATE GOAL: _____

2. ASSESS CURRENT SITUATION:

Strengths	Weaknesses	Benefits	Risks

3. BRAINSTORM APPROPRIATE ACTIONS (use this space):

4. PRIORITIZE ACTIONS: Write numbers next to actions

5. INSERT DATE GOAL IS TO BE REACHED ("target" date):_____

6. CREATE TIME LINE FOR ACTIONS:

Begin	Action	Complete by	Check when Done

7. INSERT DATE GOAL IS ACHIEVED):_____

Action Plan Form for Long Term Goals (for Reproduction)
Review Instructions Before Using

1. STATE GOAL: _____

2. ASSESS CURRENT SITUATION:

Strengths	Weaknesses	Benefits	Risks

3. BRAINSTORM APPROPRIATE ACTIONS. INCLUDE SHORT TERM GOALS AS ACTIONS
(use this space):

4. PRIORITIZE ACTIONS: Write numbers next to actions

5. INSERT DATE GOAL IS TO BE REACHED ("target" date):_____

6. CREATE TIME LINE FOR ACTIONS:

Begin	Action	Complete by	Check when Done

7. INSERT DATE GOAL IS ACHIEVED:_____

Profit Calculation Forms (for Reproduction)

PROFIT CALCULATION FORM

Title of Artwork: _____

Insert Retail Price of Artwork here (from line B or C of previous form) _____

Subtract Commission to Gallery (if any) - _____

NON-FIXED COSTS		
	Materials Costs	
	Packaging Costs	
	Selling Costs	
	Artist's Labor Costs	
	Other Labor Costs (studio assistant, framer, ?)	
	Shipping and/or Delivery Costs	
Line A	Total of Non-Fixed Costs (*enter on line B*)	

Line B   Subtract Per Unit Variable Cost (total of non-fixed costs): - _____

Line C   Subtract Average Fixed Cost (from Section 4, pg. 23): - _____

PROFIT (OR LOSS): _____

PROFIT CALCULATION FORM

Title of Artwork: _____

Insert Retail Price of Artwork here (from line B or C of previous form) _____

Subtract Commission to Gallery (if any) - _____

NON-FIXED COSTS		
	Materials Costs	
	Packaging Costs	
	Selling Costs	
	Artist's Labor Costs	
	Other Labor Costs (studio assistant, framer, ?)	
	Shipping and/or Delivery Costs	
Line A	Total of Non-Fixed Costs (*enter on line B*)	

Line B   Subtract Per Unit Variable Cost (total of non-fixed costs): - _____

Line C   Subtract Average Fixed Cost (from Section 4, pg. 23): - _____

PROFIT (OR LOSS): _____

Standard Pricing Form (for Reproduction)
For use with Pricing Method #1 only
Review Instructions Before Using

COSTS + COMMISSION + PROFIT PRICING FORM

Title of Artwork:

NON-FIXED COSTS		
	Materials Costs	
	Packaging Costs	
	Selling Costs	
	Labor Costs	
	Shipping and/or Delivery Costs	
Line A	Total of Non-Fixed Costs	

Line B Total of Non-Fixed Costs (*Line A*) = Per Unit Variable Cost:

Line C Average Fixed Cost (from previous section):

PRICE BEFORE COMMISSION AND PROFIT (*sum of lines B & C*)

COMMISSION (if any)

PROFIT

PRICE (sum of preceding three lines)

Form for Determining Fixed Costs (for Reproduction)

MY FIXED COSTS per (circle one) WEEK MONTH YEAR	

PREMISES COSTS*:		
	Studio Rent	
	Studio Mortgage	
	Maintenance / Repairs	
	Miscellaneous	
	Other	
	Other	

UTILITY COSTS*:		
	Heat	
	Electricity	
	Telephone	
	Internet Access	
	Other	

EQUIPMENT COSTS:		
	Art Tools	
Office Equipment (Computer, Copier, Printer, Scanner, etc.)		
Art Equipment (Etching Press, Darkroom Equipment, etc.)		
	Other	

INSURANCE COSTS:		
	Insurance on Premises*	
	Insurance on Artwork	
	Insurance on Artist	
	Insurance on Vehicles*	
	Other	

ADVERTISING COSTS:		
	Business Cards	
	Slides and Photos	
	Website Maintenance	
	Print Advertising	
	Other	

VEHICLE COSTS*:		
	Business Mileage	
	Maintenance & Repairs	
	Other	

Total of My Fixed Costs per Week Month Year (circle one)	

* Since many artists work in their residences and use their private vehicles for business, the items marked with asterisks may be percentages of costs normally associated with the home.

Forms for Determining Average Fixed Cost (for Reproduction)

AVERAGE FIXED COST FORM

Total Fixed Costs (from Section 4) _____

Divided by

Number of artworks produced in selected time period _____

equals

Average Fixed Cost to be assigned to a particular work* _____

*Note: The average fixed cost may need to be adjusted if a specific work takes more or less time to produce than other works made during the same period.

AVERAGE FIXED COST FORM

Total Fixed Costs (from Section 4) _____

Divided by

Number of artworks produced in selected time period _____

equals

Average Fixed Cost to be assigned to a particular work* _____

*Note: The average fixed cost may need to be adjusted if a specific work takes more or less time to produce than other works made during the same period.

Form for Determining Per Unit Variable Cost (for Reproduction)

FORM FOR DETERMINING PER UNIT VARIABLE COST	

Title of Artwork: _____

MATERIALS COSTS:		
	Canvas	
	Paper	
	Stretcher Strips	
	Paint	
	Ink	
	Pencil	
	Miscellaneous	
	Tools (brushes, etc.)	
	Other	

PACKAGING (framing?) COSTS:		
	Frame	
	Glass	
	Mat	
	Wire, Hardware, etc.	
	Other	

SELLING COSTS:		
	Travel	
	Exhibition Entry Fees	
	Gallery Fees	
	Meals with Gallery Owners or Clients	
	Commission	
	Other	
	Other	

LABOR COSTS :	Me: hourly rate: _____ x _____ (no. of hours) =	
	Studio Assistants' Wages (if any)	
	Other	

SHIPPING and/or DELIVERY COSTS:	Gas & Tolls	
Me: hourly rate: _____ x _____ (no. of hours) =		
	UPS or Fedex Charges	
	Other	

Per Unit Variable Cost (add up all above) [_____]

Daily Schedule Form - Daytime (for Reproduction)

DAILY SCHEDULE FORM - DAYTIME

TIME	Creative Activities	Marketing Activities	Personal / Non-Art Activities	Flex Time	SPECIFIC ACTIVITY
6:00					
6:30					
7:00					
7:30					
8:00					
8:30					
9:00					
9:30					
10:00					
10:30					
11:00					
11:30					
Noon					
12:30					
1:00					
1:30					
2:00					
2:30					
3:00					
3:30					
4:00					
4:30					
5:00					
5:30					

Daily Schedule Form - Nighttime (for Reproduction)

DAILY SCHEDULE FORM - NIGHTTIME

TIME	Creative Activities	Marketing Activities	Personal / Non-Art Activities	Flex Time	SPECIFIC ACTIVITY
6:00					
6:30					
7:00					
7:30					
8:00					
8:30					
9:00					
9:30					
10:00					
10:30					
11:00					
11:30					
Midnight					
12:30					
1:00					
1:30					
2:00					
2:30					
3:00					
3:30					
4:00					
4:30					
5:00					
5:30					

FOR IMMEDIATE RELEASE: «DATE»

NOTED COLLAGE ARTIST TO EXHIBIT NEW WORKS

XYZ GALLERY TO EXHIBIT WORKS BY WILLIAM PASTE

New collages by internationally known collage artist William Paste will be on display at the XYZ Gallery *(name of venue)*, 1234 Main Street, City, State *(address of venue)* from Date *(beginning date)* to Date *(ending date)*.

This will be the first local exhibit this year for Paste, whose works have been shown at the National Academy and the Museum of Modern Art in New York, have represented the U.S. overseas in exhibits sponsored by the State Department and the Smithsonian Institution, and are included in museum collections in the U.S. and Europe. Featured will be works from Paste's "Folklore Series" which are based on his experiences in the Ozarks during his childhood.

The artist, whose studio is in upstate New York, is accomplished in a variety of media. His oils, watercolors, collages, and multi-dimensional collage constructions are included in numerous public collections and have been exhibited in more than half of the fifty states and in many countries overseas. "This will be my first exhibit at the XYZ gallery," said Paste in a recent interview, " and I'm looking forward to it. I'm glad that owner Mary Smith has provided me with this opportunity to show my folklore works. I consider them to be among the best I have ever made." According to gallery owner Mary Smith, some of Paste's "Folklore Series" pieces have already found their way into museum collections. "Having Paste here to show his work is a real treat for XYZ gallery," she added.

The exhibit will be open Tuesday through Saturday from 11am to 5pm and Sunday from 1pm to 6pm. For directions call XYZ gallery at 000-000-0000.

Readers can find additional information about William Paste in Who's Who in American Art or by visiting his internet "studio" at www.pasteit.com.

* * * * * *

Enc: ☐ Photo of Artist
Sample Caption: William Paste, Internationally known Artist, to exhibit at XYZ gallery
☐ Photo of Artwork
Sample Caption: "Barbara Allen" a collage painting by internationally known artist William Paste, in exhibit at XYZ gallery
☐ Biographical Material
☐ Invitation to Opening

Press Contact for additional photos and/or information:
Cindy Paste, 7 Fancy Lane, Woodstock, NY 12498 Phone: 845-000-2222
or
Mary Smith, XYZ Gallery, 1234 Main Street, City, State, Zip Phone: 000-000-0000

FAMOUS GALLERY 400 WEST 27 STREET NEW YORK 10013 (212)345-0000
Fax: 212.345.0001
E-mail: FamousGallery@123.com
Internet: www.famousgallery.org

FOR <u>IMMEDIATE RELEASE</u>

<u>CAROL HARPER : NEW PAINTINGS</u>

<u>April 20 - May 26, 2000</u>

The Famous Gallery is pleased to present new paintings by **Carol Harper**, opening March 21, 2001 and on view through June 14, 2001.

Harper, the grand-niece of the great American painter Thomas Hart Harper**,** is best known for her subtle and evocative urban views.   These cityscapes have been the singular focus of her representational concerns for most of her 20-year career. She is represented in numerous public collections including that of the New York City Museum (New York), and the Hopewell Art Museum (Hopewell, KS), which organized the artist's first solo exhibition in 1997.

Harper's sense of pictorial space may be described as anti-architectural impressionism, revealed through the complex juxtaposition of planes and lines. She limits her subject matter to rainy days, lowering the chroma of her works. Nevertheless, her ability to flood her canvases with subtle feeling infuses a highly emotional sensibility into her work. In this exhibition, wet translucent windows and subtle oil-washed reflections further enrich delicate rain-drenched scenes that appear simultaneously real and surreal, scenes which are inspired by specific locations in Kansas City and New York, as well as those remembered and artfully rearranged according to the artist's creative sense as she develops each composition.

For further information and photographs for reproduction, please contact The Famous Gallery. Viewing hours are Tuesday through Saturday, 11:00 to 5:00

THE NEW YORK GALLERY

CONTACT: AVA BEARDSLEY
(212) 345-6789

CHRISTIAN GOODMAN

IMAGES OF FAITH
PAINTINGS ON GLASS

SAMPLE PRESS
RELEASE
C

APRIL 23 - MAY 15, 1984

Christian Goodman, noted painter and author, will present his most recent work in "Images of Faith: Paintings on Glass" at the New York Gallery from April 23 to May 15, 2002. A reception for the artist will he held on April 23 between 4:00 and 6:00 PM at the gallery.

Mr. Goodman, who's famous book *My Search for the Truth* was written in 1965, began working on this series of paintings on glass in 1992. After a decade and a half spent creating large scale environmental installations and happenings, the artist felt a need for a new direction. Always interested in working in nontraditional materials, Goodman first encountered paintings on glass as a teenager while hitch-hiking across Central Asia. First in Iran, then later in India, Yugoslavia, Senegal, Burma, and Mexico he discovered different techniques and styles of painting on glass. Ten years ago he began to adapt the techniques to his own artistic vision, and the current paintings are the result.

To create these works, various paints, glazes, and foils are applied on the reverse side of fragments of glass. The pieces are then set into a ceramic base which both supports the glass and defines the design. The colors and patterns are seen through the glass which gives them a uniformly hard and shiny appearance. In addition, while the works are flat, the materials used imbue them with an uncommon sense of mass which is essential to the power of the works.

Though Mr. Goodman's education was firmly rooted in traditional Western Art, his work for the last ten years has reflected an increasing interest in, and influence of, less traditional sources: Islamic tile work, Oriental ceramics, Hindu and Buddhist religious art, African sculpture and textiles, Contemporary "Outsider" Art, and religious rituals to name but a few. To date, he has traveled to more than 70 countries worldwide in order to experience, and discover the many elements which have in turn enriched his art. His current work reflects all of this.

1230 WEST 71st STREET, NEW YORK, NY 10021 (212)345-6789.

To: John Lindworth, Art Reviewer
The Daily Gazetteer
Los Angeles, CA 12345

FOR IMMEDIATE RELEASE

"PASTE AND PIXELS" EXHIBITION AT CORENLY GALLERY IN SANTA MONICA
INTERNATIONAL EXHIBITION EXPLORES INTERFACE OF TRADITIONAL AND DIGITAL COLLAGE
GOING DIGITAL: EXHIBITION EXPLORES TRADITIONAL AND COMPUTER-GENERATED COLLAGE

Santa Monica, CA, June 23, 2001-- Corenly Gallery in Santa Monica will host "Paste and Pixels," an exhibition which will explore the interface of traditional and digital collage, from July 14th through August 12th, 2001. The exhibit will feature collage works from the United States, Canada, England, Romania, and Japan. Included will be traditional collage works and collages generated with the help computers. Also included will be interactive works displayed on computer terminals.

"The medium of collage is flourishing," said guest curator Hope Heartwell in a recent interview, "and undergoing remarkable transition as well. While many artists still work in the traditional "cut-and-paste" manner, an increasing number of artists are "going digital" to create elements to be used in traditional collages or using computers to create entire works. This exhibition will explore the best of both worlds."

Asked why collage is attracting so much interest, Heartwell expressed her belief that it is because, unlike painting, the materials of which collages are made are often highly charged with personal, social, psychological, historic, or spiritual significance. "This gives collage works added power," said Heartwell, "affording their audiences a substantive artistic experience."

Corenly Gallery, located at 1025 Church St. in Santa Monica, is open Thursday through Sunday from 12 noon to 6 pm. For additional information call 310-000-0000 or visit www.pasteandpixels.com.

* * * * *

Press contact: Hope Heartwell, 310-123-4567 or hope@mizzentop.net

STATE ARTS AGENCIES

Your State Arts Agency is there to address your interests.
Let them know how they can help you.

Alabama State Council on the Arts
201 Monroe Street
Montgomery, AL 36130-1800
Tel: 334-242-4076 / Fax: 334-240-3269
www.arts.state.al.us

Alaska State Council on the Arts
411 West Fourth Ave. Suite 1E
Anchorage AK 99501-2343
Tel: 907-269-6610 / Toll-Free 1-888-278-7424
Fax: 907-269-6601
www.educ.state.ak.us/aksca

Arizona Commission on the Arts
417 West Roosevelt Street
Phoenix, AZ 85003
Tel: 602-255-5882 / Fax: 602-256-0282
www.arizonaarts.org

Arkansas Arts Council
1500 Tower Building
323 Center Street
Little Rock, AR 72201
Tel: 501-324-9766 / Fax: 501-324-9207
www.arkansasarts.com

California Arts Council
1300 I Street, Suite 930
Sacramento, CA 95814
Tel: 916-322-6555 or 800-201-6201
Fax: 916-322-6575
www.cac.ca.gov

Colorado Council on the Arts
1380 Lawrence Street, Suite 1200
Denver, CO 80204
Tel: 303-866-2723 / Fax: 303-866-4266
www.coloarts.state.co.us

Connecticut Commission on the Arts
One Financial Plaza
755 Main Street
Hartford, CT 06103
Tel: 860-256-2800 / Fax: 860- 256-2811
www.ctarts.org

Delaware Division of the Arts
Carvel State Office Building
820 North French Street, 4th Floor
Wilmington, DE 19801
Tel: 302-577-8278
Fax: 302-577-6561
www.artsdel.org

District of Columbia Commission on the Arts and Humanities
410 Eighth Street, NW, Fifth Floor
Washington, DC 20004
Tel: 202-724-5613
Fax: 202-727-4135
www.dcarts.dc.gov

Florida Division of Cultural Affairs
Department of State, The Capitol
1001 DeSoto Park Drive
Tallahassee, FL 32301
Tel: 850-245-6470
Fax: 850-245-6492
www.florida-arts.org

Georgia Council for the Arts
260 14th Street, NW, Suite 401
Atlanta, GA 30318
Tel: 404-685-2787
Fax: 404-685-2788
www.web-dept.com/gca

Hawai'i State Foundation on Culture and the Arts
250 South Hotel Street, 2nd Floor
Honolulu, HI 96813
Tel: 808-586-0300
Fax: 808-586-0308
www.state.hi.us/sfca

Idaho Commission on the Arts
2410 North Old Penitentiary Road
PO Box 83720
Boise, ID 83720-0008
Tel: 208-334-2119
Fax: 208-334-2488
www2.state.id.us/arts

STATE ARTS AGENCIES (continued)

Illinois Arts Council
100 West Randolph Street, Suite 10-500
Chicago IL 60601
Tel: 312-814-6750 / 800-237-6994 (IL only)
www.state.il.us/agency/iac

Indiana Arts Commission
150 W. Market Street, Suite 618
Indianapolis, IN 46204
Tel: 317-232-1268 / Fax: 317-232-5595
www.in.gov/arts/

Iowa Arts Council
Capitol Complex, 600 E. Locust
Des Moines, IA 50319-0290
Tel: 515-281-4451 / Fax: 515-242-6498
www.iowaartscouncil.org

Kansas Arts Commission
Jayhawk Tower
700 SW Jackson, Suite 1004
Topeka, KS 66603-3761
Tel: 785-296-3335 / Fax: 785-296-4989
http://arts.state.ks.us

Kentucky Arts Council
Old Capitol Annex
300 West Broadway
Frankfort, KY 40601
Tel: 502-564-3757
Toll free: 888-833-2787
www.kyarts.org

Louisiana Division of the Arts
Box 44247, 900 Riverside North
Baton Rouge LA 70804
Tel: 225-342-8180 / Fax: 225-342-8173
www.crt.state.la.us/arts

Maine Arts Commission
193 State Street
Augusta, ME 04333
Tel: 207-287-2724 / Fax: 207-287-2725
www.mainearts.com

Maryland State Arts Council
175 W. Ostend Street, Suite E
Baltimore, MD 21230
Tel: 410-767-6555 / Fax: 410-333-1062
TDD: 410-333-4519
www.msac.org

Massachusetts Cultural Council
10 St. James Avenue, 3rd Floor
Boston, MA 02116
Tel: 617-727-3668 / Fax: 617-727-0044
www.massculturalcouncil.org

Michigan Council for Arts & Cultural Affairs
702 W. Kalamazoo
PO Box 30705
Lansing, MI 48909
Tel: 517-241-4011 / Fax: 517-241-3979
www.michigan.gov/hal

Minnesota State Arts Board
Park Square Court
400 Sibley Street, Suite 200
St. Paul, MN 55101
Tel: 651-215-1600
Toll-free: 800-8MN-ARTS
Fax: 651-215-1602
www.arts.state.mn.us

Mississippi Arts Commission
239 North Lamar Street, Suite 207
Jackson, MS 39201
Tel: 601-359-6030 or 6040 / Fax: 601-359-6008
www.arts.state.ms.us

Missouri Arts Council
111 North 7th Street, Suite 105
St. Louis, MO 63101-2188
Tel: 314-340-6845 / Fax: 314-340-7215
www.missouriartscouncil.org

Montana Arts Council
City County Building
316 North Park Avenue, Suite 252
PO Box 202201
Helena, MT 59620-2201
Tel: 406-444-6430 / Fax: 406-444-6548
www.art.state.mt.us

Nebraska Arts Council
Joslyn Carriage House
3838 Davenport Street
Omaha, NE 68131-2329
Tel: 402-595-2122 / Fax: 402-595-2334
www.nebraskaartscouncil.org

STATE ARTS AGENCIES (continued)

Nevada Arts Council
716 North Carson Street, Suite A
Carson City, NV 89701
Tel: 775-687-6680 / Fax: 775-687-6688
http://dmla.clan.lib.nv.us/docs/arts

New Hampshire State Council on the Arts
2¹/₂ Beacon Street, 2nd Floor
Concord, NH 03301
Tel: 603-271-2789 / Fax: 603-271-3584
www.state.nh.us/nharts

New Jersey State Council on the Arts
225 West State Street
PO Box 306
Trenton, NJ 08625-0306
Tel: 609-292-6130 / Fax: 609-989-1440
www.njartscouncil.org

New Mexico Arts
228 East Palace Avenue
Santa Fe, NM 87501
Tel: 505-827-6490 / Fax: 505-827-6043
www.nmarts.org

New York State Council on the Arts
175 Varick Street, 3rd Floor
New York, NY 10014
Tel: 212-627-4455 / Fax: 212-620-5911
www.nysca.org

North Carolina Arts Council
Department of Cultural Resources
Jenkins House
221 East Lane Street
Raleigh, NC 27699-4632
Tel: 919-733-2821 / Fax: 919-733-4834
www.ncarts.org

North Dakota Council on the Arts
1600 East Century Avenue, Suite 6
Bismarck, ND 58503
Tel: 701-328-7590
Fax: 701-328-7595
www.state.nd.us/arts

Ohio Arts Council
727 East Main Street
Columbus, OH 43205
Tel: 614-466-2613 / Fax: 614-466-4494
www.oac.state.oh.us

Oklahoma Arts Council
Jim Thorpe Building
PO Box 52001-2001
Oklahoma City, OK 73152-2001
Tel: 405-521-2931 / Fax: 405-521-6418
www.oklaosf.state.ok.us/~arts

Oregon Arts Commission
775 Summer Street NE, Suite 200
Salem, OR 97301-1284
Tel: 503-986-0082 / Fax: 503-986-0260
www.oregonartscommission.org

Pennsylvania Council on the Arts
216 Finance Building
Harrisburg, PA 17120
Tel: 717-787-6883 / Fax: 717-783-2538
www.pacouncilonthearts.org

Rhode Island State Council on the Arts
One Capitol Hill, 3rd Floor
Providence, RI 02908
Tel: 401-222-3880
Fax: 401-222-3018
www.arts.ri.gov

South Carolina Arts Commission
1800 Gervais Street
Columbia, SC 29201
Tel: 803-734-8696 / Fax: 803-734-8526
www.state.sc.us/arts

South Dakota Arts Council
Office of the Arts
800 Governors Drive
Pierre, SD 57501-2294
Tel: 605-773-3131 / Fax: 605-773-6962
www.state.sd.us/deca/sdarts

STATE ARTS AGENCIES (continued)

Tennessee Arts Commission
Citizens Plaza, 401 Charlotte Avenue
Nashville, TN 37243-0780
Tel: 615-741-1701 / Fax: 615-741-8559
www.arts.state.tn.us

Texas Commission on the Arts
PO Box 13406, Capitol Station
Austin, TX 78711
Tel: 512-463-5535 / Fax: 512-475-2699
www.arts.state.tx.us

Utah Arts Council
617 E. South Temple Street
Salt Lake City, UT 84102
Tel: 801-236-7555 / Fax: 801-236-7556
www.arts.utah.gov

Vermont Arts Council
136 State Street, Drawer 33
Montpelier, VT 05633-6001
Tel: 802-828-3291 / Fax: 802-828-3363
www.vermontartscouncil.org

Virginia Commission for the Arts
223 Governor Street, 2nd Floor
Richmond, VA 23219
Tel: 804-225-3132 / Fax: 804-225-4327
www.arts.virginia.gov

Washington State Arts Commission
711 Capital Way S., Suite 600
PO Box 42675
Olympia, WA 98504-2675
Tel: 360-753-3860 / Fax: 360-586-5351
www.arts.wa.gov

West Virginia Commission on the Arts
1900 Kanawha Boulevard East
Charleston, WV 25305
Tel: 304-558-0240 / Fax: 304-558-2779
www.wvculture.org/arts

Wisconsin Arts Board
101 East Wilson Street, 1st Floor
Madison, WI 53702
Tel: 608-266-0190 / Fax: 608-267-0380
www.arts.state.wi.us

Wyoming Arts Council
2320 Capitol Avenue
Cheyenne, WY 82002
Tel: 307-777-7742 / Fax: 307-777-5499
http://wyoarts.state.wy.us

American Samoa Council on Culture, Arts and Humanities
PO Box 1540
Office of the Governor
Pago Pago, AS 96799
Tel: 684-633-4347 / Fax: 684-633-2059

Guam Council on the Arts & Humanities Agency
PO Box 2950
Hagatna, Guam 96932
Tel: 671-475-4226/0220 / Fax: 671-475-4227

Commonwealth Council for Arts and Culture (Northern Mariana Islands)
PO Box 5553, CHRB
Saipan, MP 96950
Tel: 670-322-9982 or 9983 / Fax: 670-322-9028

Institute of Puerto Rican Culture
PO Box 9024184
San Juan, PR 00902-4184
Tel: 787-724-0700 / Fax: 787-724-8393
www.icp.gobierno.pr

Virgin Islands Council on the Arts
41-42 Norre Gade
PO Box 103
St. Thomas, VI 00802
Tel: 340-774-5984 / Fax: 340-774-6206
www.vicouncilonarts.org

To find additional information about State Arts Councils, including names of directors, etc., visit the National Assembly of State Arts Agencies website at www.nasaa-arts.org

REGIONAL ARTS AGENCIES

Arts Midwest
2908 Hennepin Avenue, Suite 200   Minneapolis, MN 55403
Tel: 612-341-0755   Fax: 612-341-0902   www.artsmidwest.org
     States Served: IL, IN, IA, MI, MN, ND, OH, SD WI

Mid-America Arts Alliance
912 Baltimore Avenue, Suite 700   Kansas City, MO 64105
Tel: 816-421-1388   Fax: 816-421-3918   www.maaa.org
     States Served: AR, KS, MO, NE, OK, TX

Mid Atlantic Arts Foundation
201 North Charles Street, Suite 401   Baltimore, MD 21201
Tel: 410-539-6656   Fax: 410-837-5517   www.midatlanticarts.org
     States Served: DE, DC, MD, NJ, NY, PA, VA, WV

New England Foundation for the Arts
145 Tremont Street, 7th Floor   Boston, MA 02111
Tel: 617-951-0010   Fax: 617-951-0016   www.nefa.org
     States Served: CT, ME, MA, NH, RI, VT

Southern Arts Federation
1800 Peachtree St., NW, Suite 808   Atlanta, GA 30309
Tel: 404-874-7244   Fax: 404-873-2148   www.southarts.org
     States Served: AL, FL, GA, KY, LA, MS, NC, SC, TN

Western States Arts Federation
1743 Wazee Street, Suite 300   Denver, CO 80202
Tel: 303-629-1166   Fax: 303-629-9717   www.westaf.org
     States Served: AK, AZ, CA, CO, HI, ID, MT, NM, NV, OR, UT, WA, WY

NATIONAL ARTS AGENCIES

National Assembly of State Arts Agencies
1029 Vermont Avenue, NW, 2nd Floor   Washington, DC 20005
Tel: 202-347-6352   Fax: 202-737-0526   www.nasaa-arts.org

National Endowment for the Arts
1100 Pennsylvania Avenue, NW Washington, DC 20506
Tel: 202-682-5400   www.nea.gov

WHERE & WHEN TO SHOW AND OTHER OPPORTUNITIES
(PUBLICATIONS)
*Suggestion: Before you subscribe to any magazine try to find a copy to look at to make sure
that the magazine will be useful to you. Your local library can be a good resource.*

The Art Deadlines List www.artdeadlineslist.com
The Art Deadlines List is a list of competitions, contests, call for entries/papers, grants, scholarships, fellowships, jobs, internships, etc, in the arts or related areas (painting, drawing, animation, poetry, writing, music, multimedia, reporting/journalism, cartooning, dance, photography, video, film, sculpture, etc), some of which have prizes worth thousands of dollars. It is international in scope. Contests and competitions for students, K-12 and college-aged, are included. Some events/items take place on the Internet. You are invited to submit items. The list is mailed around the first of each month.

The Art Deadlines List is available in two versions: paid & free. The free version contains a smaller number of items with contact information, but shows most of the items received by paid subscribers. A subscription costs $20 for 12 once-a-month issues, sent to your email address. The Art Deadlines List is also available on paper, via US mail. The cost is $36 for 12 once-a-month issues. There is an additional charge for foreign airmail delivery. Art Deadlines List, Box 381067 Harvard Sq Stn, Cambridge MA 02238-1067, USA

Art Calendar www.artcalendar.com
The Business Magazine for Visual Artists
Art Calendar magazine is published 11x/year. Subscriptions: $33/one year, $59/two
To subscribe: call toll-free 1-866-4ARTCAL or subscribe online or send a check to P.O. Box 2675, Salisbury, MD 21802.

Articles on a wide variety of subjects related to the business of art form half of this publication. The other half consists of listings of opportunities for Exhibitions, Grants, Residencies, Publications and much more.

American Artist www.myamericanartist.com
Subs: VNU Business Publications, PO Box 15397, North Hollywood, CA 91615 Phone: 800-562-2706
12 issues (1 year): $24.95
Includes a calendar of exhibition opportunities and ads for lots of workshops.

ARTnews www.artnews.com
PO Box 2083, Knoxville, IA 50197-2083 Phone: 800-284-4625
11 issues (1 year): $39.95
Occasional listings of Opportunities... Lots of info on what's happening.

Art Times www.arttimesjournal.com
P.O. Box 730 · Mt. Marion, NY 12456 Phone: (845) 246-6944 · Fax: (845) 246-6944
11 issues (1 year): $15.00
Info on Hudson Valley, New York City and more.

Sunshine Artists www.sunshineartist.com
2600 Temple Dr. , Winter Park FL 32789-1371 1-800-804-4607
1 year: $34.95 2 years: $59.95
Lists a multitude of outdoor arts festivals. Also reviews some of them.

BOOKS ABOUT ART AND THE BUSINESS OF ART
(A RESOURCE LIST)
Suggestion: Before you buy a book, try to find a copy to look at to make sure that the book will be useful to you. Your local library can be a good resource.

The Artist in Business by Craig Dreeszen. Edited by Barbara Schaffer Bacon, John Fiscella, and Clare D. Wood. 1996. Arts Extension Service, Division of Continuing Education, University of Masachusetts, Box 31650, Amherst, MA 01003-1650 / phone: 413-545-2360
Helps artists manage their careers and set priorities on the basis of sound business practices. Geared to the needs of enterprising early career visual artists, performers, and craftspeople, the text provides a framework for acquiring fundamental skills in such essential areas as: business operations; recordkeeping, taxes, and the budget process; legal rights; and financial resources.

The Artist's Guide to New Markets: Opportunities to Show and Sell Art Beyond Galleries by Peggy Hadden. Allworth Press, 1998.
How emerging and established artists can build and expand their careers outside the gallery setting.

The Artist's Marketing & Action Plan Workbook, 5th Edition by Jonathan Talbot with Geoffrey Howard. Jonathan Talbot, 2005.
A workbook which provides the artist with a personalized marketing and action plan for selling his or her work.

The Artists' Survival Manual by Toby J. Klayman & C. Steinberg. Scribner, 1987.
Information that helps artists approach the art world with more confidence.

Art Marketing 101 by Constance Smith. Northlight Books, 2000.
Covers a wide variety of art business concerns.

Art Marketing Handbook for the Fine Artist by C. Franklin-Smith. Artnetworks, 1992.
A guide for fine artists to promotion, presentation, exhibition planning, etc.

Business and Legal Forms for Fine Artists by Tad Crawford. Allworth Press, New York, 1995.
> Contains a number of useful forms one can photocopy. Covers many different aspects of the art business.

The Business of Being an Artist by Daniel Grant. Allworth Press, New York, 1996.
> Covers a wide range of art world concerns in a candid way. Lot's of quotes from established artists.

The Business of Art by Lee Caplin. Prentice Hall in cooperation with the National Endowment for the Arts, 1998.
> As well as writings by the author, this book includes a collection of essays by different artists and other members of the arts community on everything from *preparing for an art career* to *estate planning for artists.*

The Fine Artist's Guide to Marketing and Self-Promotion by Julius Vitali. Allworth Press, New York, 1996.
> An anecdotal look at a variety of marketing and promotion concerns for artists.

How to Survive and Prosper as an Artist by Caroll Michels. Owl Books, 5th Rev edition, December, 2001.
> A guide to taking control of your career and making a good living in the art world.

New York Contemporary Art Galleries by Renée Phillips. Manhattan Arts Intrnational, New York, updated annually. Available from Manhattan Arts International, 200 E 72nd Street, Suite 26L, New York, NY 10021. Phone: 212-472-1660 E-mail: manarts@aol.com
> An annual look at the galleries of New York... Who owns them, who they are showing, their selection process for new artists, their addresses, and more.

Taking the Leap by Cay Lang. Chronicle Books, 1998.
> A step-by-step guide to jumpstarting your career as an artist.

This book was printed and bound by Royal Fireworks Press, Unionville, NY.
The majority of the book was set in a contemporary version of
Garamond, a typeface inspired by the designs of
the 16th century French type designer
Claude Garamond.
Book designed
by
Jonathan Talbot.